Foiled Creative Fire
A study of remarkable women with breast cancer

Foiled Creative Fire

A study of remarkable women with breast cancer

HEATHER GOODARE

Foreword by Professor Michael Dixon OBE

'Childless women get it,
And men when they retire;
It's as if there had to be some outlet
For their foiled creative fire.'

W. H. Auden, 'Miss Gee' (1937)*

Ashwood Books

By the same Author

Fighting Spirit: the Stories of Women in the Bristol Breast Cancer Survey (Scarlet Press 1996)

★'Miss Gee' is by W. H. Auden, and appears on pp. 160-1 of his Collected Poems edited by Edward Mendelson (Faber & Faber, 2004, ISBN 9780571221448). The book's body text is set in Bembo and the headings are Avenir Next.

First published in Australia 2020 by Ashwood Books
PO Box 73, Franklin, Tasmania 7113

Printed by Lightning Source

Paperback ISBN: 978-0-9874111-5-0
Kindle ISBN: 978-0-9874111-6-7

This book is dedicated to the home care staff
of the City of Edinburgh Council,
without whose help it would probably not have been finished.

'This is a remarkable and unique book… Heather Goodare has written the book about breast cancer that is long overdue… We must learn from the tragic errors of the past so this would be a book I would recommend to young clinicians embarking on their journey to understand the nature of breast cancer and the needs of the women diagnosed with the disease.'

Professor Michael Baum ChM, MD, FRCS
Professor Emeritus of Surgery and Visiting Professor of Medical Humanities
University College London

✧ ✧ ✧ ✧ ✧

'I thoroughly enjoyed this meticulously researched and eminently readable book by Heather Goodare… I found the connections between mental health, in particular stress, and the onset of cancer extremely interesting. In our modern world, where women are continually blamed for their own breast cancer i.e. by not following the perceived wisdom of adequate exercise and a healthy diet, it is refreshing to have 'evidence' from history that lifestyle factors outwith our control may have been confounding factors for hundreds of years.'

Moira Adams, MA Hons, Trustee of Breast Cancer Prevention Scotland

✧ ✧ ✧ ✧ ✧

'… so exciting and well written that it reads like a novel… The publication of this book comes at one of the key moments in our societies, which are finally moving, overwhelmed by women's demands and anger towards abuse and inequality, but also by the progressive de-escalation of treatment morbidity… The current achievement is that patients are now teachers in health schools and sit on medical research committees… Contemporary psychosocial oncology is now fully integrated into treatments.'

Patrice Guex
Honorary Professor, School of Medicine and Biology, CHUV (Centre hospitalier universitaire vaudois)

Foreword

STRESS, ANXIETY AND DEPRESSION in our society seem to be increasing. There also seem to be more patients undergoing treatment for these conditions and a large number of patients who once they start medication, take it for life. It is not surprising therefore that increasingly people are asking 'what is the effect of stress, anxiety and depression on the body and how does it influence various conditions including cancer?' Cancer Research UK accept that stressful events alter the levels of circulating hormones in the body and affect the immune system. Anti-depressant drugs themselves can influence levels of hormones, particularly prolactin. Despite these apparent changes, one large study of 100,000 women in the UK in 2016 suggested no consistent evidence of stress causing breast cancer, but this study did not look specifically at anxiety or depression. Intriguingly this study did note a positive association between divorce, a significantly stressful life event, and an increase in ER negative breast cancer. Another study of stressful events and their association with breast cancer from 2003 reported that divorce/separation, death of a husband and death of a close relative or friend were all factors associated with an increased risk of breast cancer. In clinical practice one often sees patients who have had traumatic lives and who have experienced traumatic events such as divorce. It is clear that there is evidence that certain significant life events do appear to be associated with an increased breast cancer risk.

There have been a variety of randomized trials correlating survival and psychotherapy. Research has shown that giving cancer patients information in a support group helps to reduce tension, anxiety and tiredness and lowers the risk of depression. Psychotherapy and support groups also improve quality of life, but as yet there is no clear evidence that support groups and other forms of psychotherapy help people with breast cancer survive longer. This may surprise readers because psychotherapy has been shown to significantly improve the number of natural killer cells in the body and these are known to have anticancer activity. Psychotherapy reduces chronic stress and reduces cortisol and improves hormonal profile. The major problem in trying to identify the effects of stress, anxiety and depression is the multifactorial nature of breast cancer risk and prognosis, and isolating one factor statistically is extremely difficult. Thus, despite the evidence in the literature indicating that reducing stress might not influence the incidence of breast cancer or the outlook, one is left with the feeling that this may not be the whole story.

Against this background comes this fascinating book that gives insight into the lives of many famous women through history who have had breast cancer. This book looks at these women and their backgrounds, their life events and their subsequent anxiety and depression, and raises again the issue of how the mind and the body interact and how traumatic lives and events interrelate to breast cancer and survival. This book is immensely readable and enjoyable. History teaches us so much and is so interesting. Reading this book I learned so much. An insight into people's lives, and particularly famous people, is always fascinating. Discussed in the book is how some women with apparently advanced cancer survived. The stories also testify how brave these women were, some having had breast cancer surgery without anaesthesia, which today would be unthinkable. Why did some of these famous women with apparently advanced breast cancer survive and others succumb? Is it their indomitable spirit, or is it the biology of their disease? It's also worth noting that, in the past, diagnosis was not as reliable as it is today, and women have been given mastectomies when their 'tumour' was most likely only a cyst. In any case, the tales of these individuals are remarkable. The story of each woman is totally absorbing. As a surgeon who looks after women with breast cancer, it is patients' stories that make my work so rewarding. It is not just the patient one looks after but it is also their family and everybody around them. This is not just a book of the stories of individual women with breast cancer, it is an insight into their lives, what happened to these women, and the effect breast cancer had on them. I know you will find these stories as interesting as I have and at the end you might come to understand why the interaction of the body and the mind is as fascinating now as it was when Homer, and Socrates, wrote about it two thousand years ago.

Professor J Michael Dixon, OBE
Professor of Breast Surgical Oncology and Consultant Surgeon

Contents

The second dates given are those on which breast cancer was diagnosed

Acknowledgements

MANY PEOPLE HAVE HELPED with this book, which has been simmering away for a long time. First and foremost I want to thank Penelope Goodare, my stepdaughter, who did a wonderful job on copy-editing before the MS was sent to the publisher, and also compiled the index. The historian David Arnold helped to shorten the chapter on Vicky, the Empress Victoria, which was originally much too long. Professor Michael Baum lent me the book on which Chapter 2 is based. My old friend from Oxford days, Dr Karina Williamson, with whom I was reunited on my removal to Edinburgh, helped with the chapter on Christina Rossetti, and various other friends found themselves looking at other chapters as they were finished: Liz Humphreys, my brother Dr John Young, my stepson Professor Julian Goodare, Dr Charlotte Williamson OBE, Janice Millington, Chair of RAGE (Radiotherapy Action Group Exposure), Elizabeth Jogee, my son Dr Julian Károlyi and his wife Emma Károlyi, Joe Boyle, and Avis Lewallen. My niece, Dr Susan Young, gave some final help before the book was published. Finally, Duncan Wilson kindly helped me to sort out some computer problems. If I have forgotten any of you, please forgive me. This book has been a long time in the making.

I am warmly grateful to Professor Michael Dixon, whom I first met when we were both on the Editorial Board of the *British Medical Journal*, for his generous Foreword: I felt quite safe when I moved to Edinburgh and was under his care — until he said he didn't need to see me any more! I am also very grateful to Gerard Dugdill, Publishing Director, Pink Ribbon, the network for breast cancer prevention and cure, whom I met at a breast cancer conference a while ago: he has been encouraging me to keep going.

Finally, I should like to thank Jonathan Sturm, of Ashwood Books, for his help and guidance.

Heather Goodare

Introduction

W.H. Auden was not the first, and by no means the last, to observe the connection between cancer and personality, or cancer and life events. Galen, in the second century AD, observed that 'melancholic' women were predisposed to breast cancer, and this theme was echoed by Gendron (1701)[1], Guy (1759)[2], and Walshe (1846)[3]. Today we could surmise that traumatic life events such as divorce, bereavement, or redundancy, tend to trigger long-term anxiety and depression, which in turn, in those with other risk factors, may affect the immune system and give rise to cancer.

Lawrence LeShan[4] goes further and identifies a particular kind of person who develops a certain way of dealing with stress, which arises in response to early childhood trauma. The child is powerless and defenceless in the face of abuse, whether physical or mental, and if there is no one offering sympathy and support, becomes unable to express the pain. The only way of coping is to develop a protective carapace, remaining outwardly calm and even capable. Then when a stressful situation develops for the second time in adulthood, once again the person copes, but the body pays the price. Typically, the person finds that life has lost its lustre, that creativity is stifled, and that there is no way out of the impasse. In other words, creative fire is foiled.

When cancer develops, some people accept it as a death sentence, as a tunnel with no light at the end. However, according to LeShan, there may be a way out. (Since my theme is women with breast cancer, from now on the person will be *the woman*.) If the woman can regain her joy in life, and sing her own song, in LeShan's inspiring phrase, then, he argues, she will also be able to regain health. He quotes several case histories to illustrate this thesis.

Breast cancer is not a new disease, even though its incidence is on the increase. Many factors may be at work: family history, early menarche, late menopause, diet, smoking, environmental factors such as pesticides (particularly endocrine disrupters), cosmic radiation, oral contraceptives, hormone replacement therapy, obesity, and so on. As the list gets longer it also gets more modern. While the first four risk factors listed here could be said to be relevant for all recorded history, the rest are relatively recent hazards that may possibly account for the increased incidence.

However, in my own work as a counsellor, time and again I have heard women say: 'You know, I think it all started when my husband walked out'; 'when my son went to prison'; 'when I lost my job'; 'when my mother was diagnosed with Alzheimer's and I had to look after her'; 'when my disabled child was born'. The theme running through these stories was a feeling of being trapped, of not being able to do one's own thing or sing one's own song. What I tried to do as a counsellor was to encourage people to reclaim their creativity, in whatever form was appropriate for them.

In looking at women in history who had suffered from breast cancer, I was intrigued to discover how and why some of them survived and some did not. I found, to my surprise, that some made remarkable recoveries, without the benefits of modern medicine. Surgery without anaesthetic must have been a gruelling experience, but some survived in spite of it. The story of the novelist Fanny Burney is well known. Her mastectomy was performed in 1811 by Napoleon's famous army surgeon Baron Larrey, and she then outlived her husband and her son, only dying 29 years later at the ripe old age of 87, and not apparently of breast cancer. Though her creativity was in decline, according to her biographer Kate Chisholm 'she never lost her faith or her spirited outlook on life'.[5] Somehow she continued to 'sing her own song'. Was this the key to her survival?

The more I studied women in history with breast cancer the more this theme fascinated me. Why did some survive and others not? Was it that those who died had cancers that were further advanced at the time of diagnosis? Were their doctors less competent? Or was it something to do with themselves, their personalities, their lack of fighting spirit? Did some of the survivors simply not have cancer in the first place?

This theory has been put to me several times by some sceptics, who pointed out that 18th- and 19th-century doctors did not have the resources of modern pathological laboratories at their disposal, and could not have made reliable diagnoses. While accepting that diagnosis in the past was less reliable than it is today, and we can never know for sure the truth about historical cases, I have assumed that the information we have is correct. The editor of Fanny Burney's diary, which gives her own account of her mastectomy, notes that according to a Dr Rocke Robertson, 'The symptoms that FBA describes do not suggest a malignancy; for pain, which was the prominent feature noted a full year before the operation, is most uncommon in curable cancer of the breast.'[6] Though uncommon, pain is not an inadmissible symptom in breast cancer, as I know from personal experience, and in a woman of 59 the cancer is less likely to have been fast-growing than in a younger woman. Also, a surgeon of Larrey's reputation and experience would probably have known the difference between a malignant tumour and a benign lump, even given the limited resources of the time. Moreover, Larrey was assisted by six other doctors, including the pupil who wrote up the notes of the operation. According to this account, the tumour was the size of a fist, adhering to the main pectoral muscle [*pectoralis major*].[7] Baron Larrey himself must surely have checked these notes, and they seem very convincing. Then again, even modern doctors sometimes get it wrong.

So I am making the assumption that if contemporary writers say that a woman has a cancer of the breast, so it probably was. Given this, what sort of woman was she? What was her personality? Was she subjected to chronic stress? If so, how did she deal with this stress? Was she able to come through her experience and find her own voice again, or find a new voice? Did she survive for a reasonable time, or did she die soon after diagnosis? *What was her story?*

I should say that I might well have added several more women to the list: Mary Anning, for example, who was born in 1799, in Lyme Regis, Dorset, whose father died when she was 11 years old. Several of her brothers and sisters also died in childhood, but Mary survived, to become an accomplished geologist, in spite of her working-class background and poor education, selling fossils that she collected locally. She was not allowed to attend meetings of the Geological Society of London, let alone university. All the same, she would astonish experts with her knowledge of fossils. She died of breast cancer at the age of 47 on 9th March 1847.

Nearer to our own time, another woman who illustrates my theme well is Dusty Springfield. Born in London in 1939, just before the outbreak of the Second World War, she was brought up as a Roman Catholic, by parents who often quarrelled, and Dusty had 'no recollection of warmth or affection'.[8] She left her Catholic school at the age of 16, and launched into the world of pop. Her career progressed well as a blues singer, but stress took its toll. She spent several years in California, where she drank to excess, took drugs, and had breakdowns in the studio. Eventually she acknowledged that she was bisexual, returned to England, and was awarded the OBE. But the same year (1999) she lost her life to breast cancer.

There is, I am sure, plenty of scope for further study of women in history with breast cancer. This book is just a beginning.

Notes and References

1.   D. Gendron: Inquiries into the nature, knowledge and cure of cancer (London, 1701).
2.   R. Guy: Essay on squirrhous tumours and cancer (London, W. Owen, 1759).
3.   W.H. Walshe: The nature and treatment of cancer (London, Taylor & Walton, 1846).
4.   Lawrence LeShan: Cancer as a turning point (Bath, Gateway, 1989).
5.   Kate Chisholm: Fanny Burney: her life (London, Vintage, 1999), p. 28.
6.   J. Hemlow et al. (eds): The Journals and Letters of Fanny Burney (Madame d'Arblay), 1791–1840 (12 vols, Oxford, Oxford University Press, 1972–84), Vol.VI, p. 607n.
7.   *ibid.*, p. 61.
8.   Lucy O'Brien: Dusty: a biography of Dusty Springfield (Sidgwick & Jackson, London, 1988; Pan Books, London, 2000), p. 5.

Anne of Austria, Queen of France

ANNE CAME FROM THE POWERFUL Habsburg dynasty (hence the name 'Anne of Austria'), and was born into the Spanish branch of the royal family in 1601. The court had moved from Madrid to Vallodolid before her birth, and remained there until 1606, when it moved back to Madrid. In 1601 Elizabeth I was still on the English throne, and at war with Spain. Anne's father was Philip III, King of Spain, and her grandfather was Philip II, the son of Emperor Charles V of Austria-Hungary, Head of the Holy Roman Empire, who had also been married to Queen Mary Tudor of England. Anne's mother was Margaret, sister of the Emperor Ferdinand II. When Anne, the eldest daughter, was born, the Empire had passed its peak: when Philip I assumed the throne the Spanish dominions included the Netherlands, Franche-Comté, Naples, Sicily, Milan and Sardinia, but during the 17th century these possessions were slowly eroded and the power of Spain dwindled.

At the end of the 16th century the Spanish population was in decline, owing to the disastrous plague of 1599–1600. Castile was weary, depressed and disillusioned. The Spanish Armada had been defeated by the English, who had also sacked Cádiz. The American colonies were now self-sufficient and no longer needed Spanish imports. It was a time of crisis. There was a huge gap between rich and poor, and ambitious men found the Church a satisfactory refuge that would be sure to provide at least food and shelter, if not advancement.

When Philip III acceded to the throne in 1598 he was only 20; his health was poor, and he relied heavily on advisers. His favourite, the Duke of Lerma, was the virtual ruler, together with the Junta that he established. The move to Vallodolid was probably because Lerma wanted to get Philip away from the influence of his powerful grandmother, the Empress Maria, who returned to Spain after the death of her husband Maximilian II to become a nun in a Madrid convent. Cervantes published the first part of *Don Quixote* in 1605: tilting at windmills was an apt metaphor for the manner in which affairs of state were conducted.

For a princess at such a time her prime duty was to make a successful marriage with a significant royal family, so as to consolidate alliances. Anne was brought up in a very disciplined manner, taught to obey and be mindful of her responsibilities, paying great attention to religious ceremonials and observances. In Catholic Spain as a member of the royal family these must have been onerous. When Anne was only ten her mother died: so she was no doubt thereafter in the hands of governesses and of course her father, and we can guess that this was hard for her emotionally. We don't know what support, if any, she was given when going through puberty. At the age of only 14, she was exiled from home and father on her marriage to Louis XIII in 1615. At the same time her brother, later Philip IV, married the Princess Elisabeth, sister to Louis XIII. With such a double alliance no doubt it was hoped that France and Spain would remain firm friends.

Louis XIII was the same age as Anne, and though her marriage was probably consummated on her wedding night, she was thereafter rejected by Louis and went through years of unhappiness and uncertainty, subjected to daily humiliation and badly treated by Richelieu, who in 1616 became a secretary of state to the King, and in 1622 was made a cardinal. He was appointed her 'almoner', so she was no doubt dependent on him for her expenses. She was also eclipsed by her very powerful Florentine mother-in-law, Marie de' Medici, who had taken over as Queen Regent when her husband Henry IV was murdered in 1610, and her son Louis was nine years old. However, when Louis reached the age of 16 he asserted his authority and banished his mother to Blois, where she stayed for two years. Richelieu achieved a reconciliation between the two in 1621, when Marie resumed her place in the royal council, but she continued to intrigue, and was finally exiled to Brussels in 1631.

It seems that it was only when Anne reached the age of 18 that marital relations with Louis were resumed. Louis was an enigma: it is said that he was somewhat backward and ill-educated. It seemed too that his sexuality was ambivalent: he had male favourites with whom he lived 'intimately', notably Henri d'Effiat, marquis de Cinq-Mars. He was also rumoured to have had several mistresses, among them Mademoiselle de la Fayette and Madame d'Hautefort. No wonder his life with Anne was problematic.

When Anne was still only 20 her father died, in 1621. Now she was alone in a foreign country, with no close relatives to support her, sustained only by her piety. Alexandre Dumas in his historical romance *The Three Musketeers* gives her a Spanish companion, but as far as we know she had no one.

In 1624 Richelieu became a member of the King's Council, and shortly afterwards, chief minister. Between 1628 and 1635 he consolidated his system of European alliances and planned to free France from the Habsburg hegemony. As a Habsburg, Anne stood in his way, and he successfully drove a wedge between her and the King, who needed little encouragement to seek his pleasures elsewhere.

This made it even more difficult for Anne to achieve her most important mission: to produce an heir. She managed to become pregnant, but miscarried in March 1622. She also suffered a bad fall in 1623: she must have been under tremendous strain. In 1626 she was falsely accused of plotting against her husband, and during the years 1627–37 it was clear that Louis valued Richelieu more than his wife. In 1637 Richelieu discovered that she was secretly corresponding with the Spanish rulers. Anne lived in constant fear of being repudiated and sent back to Spain. She seemed unable to stand up for herself in face-to-face encounters with Louis.

There followed many more childless years: it was not until 1638, when Anne was already 37, that her son Louis was born. There was great rejoicing: at last the king had an heir, and Anne had fulfilled her role. The young Louis became king at the age of four on the death of his father in May 1643, and Anne now came into her own, as Queen Regent. Together with her minister Cardinal Mazarin, who succeeded Richelieu on his death in 1642, she now ruled the kingdom. She also had a second son, Philippe, born in 1640.

The life pattern of some women at risk of breast cancer already takes shape. Early bereavements, separation from parents, repression of emotions, an unhappy marriage, and late childbirth. As was the custom in royal households, Anne did not breast-feed her child (another risk factor for breast cancer): this duty was assigned to a wet-nurse. The joy and triumph of bearing this first child, so longed-for, must have been tainted by the knowledge of her husband's infidelities. But now her mission was to bring up the child as a royal prince, soon to be King.

It was only after her husband died that she could begin to fulfil her true self and give expression to her creativity. She is described as 'one of the great beauties of the age' according to Madame de Motteville: blonde, full-bosomed, and strong, with large attractive eyes. She was said to eat and drink like a man: there is a suggestion that over-nutrition (a further risk factor for breast cancer) gave rise to a complexion slightly blemished by acne. Her portrait shows the typical Habsburg features, especially the somewhat bulbous nose, but she still appears handsome. She was not highly educated, but she was used to overcoming obstacles, showing wisdom and good judgement, even though at first she must have felt somewhat overwhelmed by her new responsibilities. Mazarin was appointed her prime minister, and under his guidance France pursued a successful foreign policy. This however involved war against the Spaniards, against her own younger brother Philip IV: France had declared war against Spain in 1635, before the birth of her son Louis, and peace was only finally negotiated in 1659. This surely caused Anne great stress and anxiety. At a time when she must have wanted her Spanish family to celebrate the long-awaited birth of her son, her country was at war with theirs. But she kept her counsel.

During the years 1648 to 1652 civil war came to disturb France, and was given the name 'Fronde', meaning 'sling', because during the disturbances the windows of Cardinal Mazarin's party were pelted with stones by the Paris mob. The movement was originally aimed at redressing grievances, but it degenerated into a squabble between various nobles who sought to overthrow Mazarin. In the end, after years of anarchy, the King's party was hailed as the source of order and settled government, and Mazarin regained power. Throughout this period Anne kept her nerve and ensured the stability of the royal house: she remained Regent until 1659, when Louis gained his majority and began to rule. This was no mean achievement for Anne.

The dynastic alliances continued. As part of the peace settlement with Spain in 1659 Philip IV's daughter Maria Teresa (Anne's niece) was married to Louis, bringing a dowry of 500,000 escudos, full payment being a condition of Maria Teresa's renunciation of future claims to the Spanish throne. At the time Mazarin knew that the Spanish treasury was in a dire state, and in fact the dowry was never paid. In the summer of 1660 a ceremony to consolidate the peace and conclude negotiations was held, on the border between France and Spain. After a separation of 45 years, Anne was reunited with her brother Philip. Impetuously she threw etiquette to the winds and rushed forward to embrace him. But Philip was scandalized by this public demonstration of affection, and turned his face away. Poor Anne: what a rejection! After all she had done to bring the two countries together after their long enmity! She must have longed for reconciliation with her brother, and his cold reception must have hurt her. No doubt from his point of view she had learned frivolous French habits.

There was one however who did gain her affection. Anne and Mazarin became very close, and it was rumoured that they were secretly married. Her correspondence with him certainly indicates intimacy. Since she was genuinely devout, 'living in sin' would have been unlikely. But the combination of their talents assured the unity of France and the security of its throne for her son.

It is worth looking more closely at this relationship. Mazarin came from a Sicilian family, and was born at Piscina in the Abruzzi in 1602, making him a year younger than Anne. He was educated by Jesuits in Rome, and then went to Spain, where he distinguished himself more by his gambling and amorous adventures than by his study. However, he acquired a thorough understanding of both the Spanish language and Spanish gallantry. Back in Rome in 1622 he took a law degree, then became a captain of infantry. After successful diplomatic service for the Pope he was presented to two canonries, though he had not been ordained priest.

He then accepted Richelieu's offer of service at the French court, and in 1639 acquired French citizenship. Further successful diplomatic service was rewarded by promotion to the rank of cardinal in 1641. In 1642 Richelieu died and Mazarin took his place. Very cleverly he had made himself indispensable to both King and Queen. His Spanish gallantry towards Anne paid off. Moreover they were able to converse in her native language.

Though his foreign policy was brilliant, at home he became too greedy, and was hated by both bourgeois and nobles. He also jealously guarded the Queen from everyone except his own cronies. Then came the Fronde, already mentioned, which forced Mazarin into exile for a year. Finally he founded a royal party to support Louis XIV, Anne kept her nerve, and the revolution fizzled out.

Did he marry Anne? This was not impossible since he had only taken minor orders, which could be relinquished: he was never ordained priest, nor had he taken a vow of celibacy. That there was affection, even passion between them, is clear. He knew how to gain her heart, and he knew her heart's desire was to see her son reigning successfully on the throne of France.

Their correspondence was certainly intimate. Here is an example of Anne's letters to Mazarin, during his exile.

...I no longer know when to expect your return, since every day brings obstacles to prevent it. All I can say is that I am very upset about it and bear this delay with great impatience... I have received your letters almost every day, and without that I do not know what would happen. Continue to write to me as often...[1]

When Mazarin died in March 1661 he was still only 59. The Queen was 60. It must have been a terrible blow to her, whether or not they were married. Once again, as in childhood, she suffered the pangs of bereavement, but this time she was losing a true friend and counsellor, her equal as well as possibly her lover. They had known each other for twenty years—longer than many marriages.

Sadly, Anne's son Louis took after his philandering father, much to her grief and dismay. According to state protocol he married his cousin the Spanish Infanta Maria Teresa in 1659, rather than the niece of Mazarin, who attracted him, but he was soon having extra-marital affairs, which Anne did her best to keep from her daughter-in-law. Maria Teresa did not have the same strength of spirit that was shown by Anne: in addition to Louis' infidelities she also suffered the death of two infants. But in affairs of state Louis was highly successful. After the death of Mazarin he decided to be his own first minister, and turned out to be a clever diplomat, conscientious ruler, and great patron of the arts: his 73-year reign until 1715 was the longest recorded in European history. He surely earned the title 'Grand Monarque', and his mother would have been proud of him.

Anne had always been strong and healthy, but in Easter 1663 she became ill with a strange fever, with nausea, and pain in her legs. She recovered, but in May 1664 she began to feel pain in her left breast, where she discovered a lump. She ignored it since she was preoccupied with her children's marital affairs and matters of state. In November Maria Teresa gave birth prematurely to a child who later died: Maria herself was very ill. Finally Anne consulted her doctors, who examined her: she guessed from their faces that it was a cancer. By this time it was incurable, with extensive local spread. A mastectomy was not proposed (though there were precedents for such a procedure), but her doctors prescribed bleeding, enemas and purges, with an ointment to relieve the pain in her breast. The final solution was an arsenic paste, applied so as to harden the diseased tissue, which was then cut away. She suffered repeated operations from August 1665 to January 1666.

She took her illness as a penance, thinking that God was punishing her for being vain and having cared too much for her body. Towards the end she confessed daily. She died with Philippe at her side on 20th January 1666. Louis could not face the end, though he had faithfully stayed with her, camping out on a mattress in her room throughout the last stages of her illness, nursing her with devotion and performing intimate services such as changing her linen. He left the room, leaving Philippe with his mother.

Since Anne's breast cancer was diagnosed late, it is hardly surprising that she did not recover, in spite of the best efforts of her doctors using the remedies available at the time. At this stage of the disease, even with the chemotherapy we have in the 21st century, all one can hope for is to gain a few months' remission, and the last distasteful measures taken by Anne's doctors in the form of repeated cutting away of the diseased tissue do actually seem to have given her a short remission. Her faith was such an important part of her life that this too must have helped by giving her last months meaning and purpose.

Anne had been a frequent visitor at the Convent of the Val de Grace, and she had seen nuns dying of breast cancer in the infirmary there: she knew what to expect. Breast cancer, then as now, was not an uncommon disease, and even then was recognized to afflict certain categories of women in particular. Nuns were especially susceptible. So how did their lifestyles put them at greater risk? The main factor seems to have been childlessness, a natural consequence of taking a vow of chastity. I would suggest also that the emotional deprivation and suppression of feelings inevitably involved in renouncing normal family life and being subjected to monastic discipline may also be a factor, in line with the theme of this book.

Select Bibliography

Ruth Kleinman:	*Anne of Austria, Queen of France* (Ohio State University Press, Columbus, 1985)
Alain Decaux:	*Histoire des Françaises: I la Soumission* (Libraire Académique Perrin, Paris, 1972), especially chapter x, 'Vent de fronde pour les dames'
Correspondence between Anne of Austria and her brother Ferdinand:	Bibliothèque Nationale: Fonds Français 3747 fols. 1–44: 1634–7
Letters to Mazarin:	Bibliothèque Nationale: Fonds Clairembault 1144 fols. 88–101v.

Notes

1. Quoted in Kleinman, p. 227.

Soeur Marie Barbier de l'Assomption

THE EXTRAORDINARY STORY OF SISTER Marie is found in a biography of Michel Sarrazin (1659–1735), who is described as 'A Canadian biologist' on the title page of his biography by Arthur Vallée, Professor of Medicine in the University of Laval, published in 1917. Sarrazin was both physician and surgeon. This brief account is all we have in the way of source material for this story, but it is certainly worth telling. It fills in the historical gap between Anne of Austria and our next subject, Fanny Burney, and also marks the progress of surgery during this period.

Michel Sarrazin, physician and surgeon.

A contemporary note quoted in the biography of Michel Sarrazin, who practised in Quebec, reads:

> In spring 1700 Sister Marie Barbier de l'Assomption came down from Montreal to be treated for her breast cancer by M. Sarrazin. She had already been treated earlier, in 1698, for the same problem. Since then it had grown considerably, which prompted her to return, and after some preparations M. Sarrazin, both a skilled surgeon and an experienced physician, operated on her on 29th May: this was the only remedy that would prevent her death. She returned in the autumn to Montreal completely cured.[1]

This patient of Sarrazin is from many points of view exceptionally interesting. She was in fact the deputy superior of her convent, and during her long rule in the community she undertook several important responsibilities. Known for her great piety, she had a reputation among her sisters of saintliness, discipline, and devotion to duty.

The tumour she suffered and which the surgeon treated was attributed to her penitential lifestyle. Perhaps this was the reason that Sarrazin did not intervene on her first visit, thinking that it was a benign lesion. She later became convinced of the severity of her problem, but was also resigned to it. For a long time she suffered discomfort, continuing to function, until Monseigneur de Saint-Valier (her confessor?) advised her to see M. Sarrazin again, given the rapid advance of her condition since 1698.

She underwent medical treatment, which had no effect. Very probably Sarrazin tried herbal remedies to which curative properties were attributed: Arum cadense was used to treat tumours, as well as Aster corona. But lack of success confirmed him in his final opinion that surgery was necessary.

When in 1700 Sister Marie returned to the Hôtel-Dieu hospital in Quebec to consult Sarrazin her state seemed desperate, and there was nothing else but to attempt surgery as a last resort. Sarrazin saw her the day she arrived, and could only observe the progress of her disease. 'Whatever course I take', he said, 'I see the sister of the Assumption in danger of approaching death. If one doesn't operate she will certainly die in a few days, her pain increasing as one watches, but attempting an operation would almost certainly be a death sentence, since one could scarcely hope that she could endure it, and even less that she could recover.'[2]

But in spite of everything he decided on surgery, prepared for the procedure with local treatment, and proceeded to perform a mastectomy ten days later, after having himself taken communion, as a good Christian, in company with his patient and the whole Hôtel-Dieu community.

The results were entirely favourable, after a brief scare during the course of convalescence, and Sister Marie Barbier made pious pilgrimages to Our Lady of Loretto and St Joseph of Lévy, to give thanks for her healing.

Returning to her community, she took up her full duties again during the following year, and for 19 years afterwards continued her work of charity and education. She died in 1739 at the age of 79.

It is interesting to follow Sarrazin's practice with this patient, observing his medical tact, his professional expertise, his surgical skill, and his lofty religious and moral conscience. Also remarkable is the persistence of his patient, and the huge effort she made to consult a reputable and competent professional, at considerable personal cost. A few months later, Sarrazin performed the same operation on another nun. The archive of the Hôtel-Dieu records several important procedures performed by him. It seems that Sarrazin's array of skills, together with Sister Marie's strong faith and the support of her convent, combined to overcome the cancer, which had progressed to an advanced stage before surgery.

Unmarried nuns are well known by doctors to be at greater risk of breast cancer than married women, especially those who bear children at a young age. Sister Marie's creativity was manifest in her charitable and educational works, and as soon as she could return to them after her surgery this is what she did, living a productive and creative life for another 19 years. The role of spirituality in her recovery one can only surmise, but the recent adoption of 'mindfulness' in medical circles seems to indicate that contemporary medical thinking is coming round to the opinion that the mind can indeed help to heal the body.

Notes

1.   Translated from Arthur Vallée, Professeur à la faculté de médecine de l'université Laval: *Un biologiste Canadien: Michael Sarrazin 1659–1735* (Québec, Ls-A. Proulx, 1927), pp. 61–2.

2.   *ibid.*, p. 63.

Acknowledgement

I am particularly indebted to the eminent breast cancer surgeon Michael Baum for drawing my attention to the amazing story of Sister Marie, and for lending me the book acknowledged above, which is my sole source for it.

Fanny Burney

FRANCES BURNEY (1752–1840) WAS THE
second daughter of Dr Charles Burney
(1726–1814), according to Grove's
Dictionary of Music and Musicians 'one
of the most famous of musical his-
torians'. His name was originally
MackBurney, and his family came
from Scotland. He was an accomplished musician working in London,
playing the organ, giving harpsichord
lessons, assisting Handel rehears-
ing singers for oratorios and operas,
and generally known about town.
He married Esther Sleepe in 1749
(somewhat late since their first child
Hetty had already been born), and he
took several musical appointments in London, until he became ill and the family
moved to King's Lynn to escape the grimy air of the metropolis. There he became
organist of St Margaret's Church, and there Fanny was born.

Apparently she was slow in learning her letters, shy and retiring, though her
mother did not doubt her intelligence. She had a phenomenal memory, but was
not particularly musical, unlike the rest of the family: her older sister Hetty, then
Susan, who was three years younger, and her brothers James and Charles. Very
sadly, her mother died when Fanny was only ten, shortly after giving birth to a
daughter, Charlotte. This must have been a bad time for Fanny, as she had been
very close to her mother. Here, then, was the first emotional trauma for Fanny:
the loss of her mother, who had been for her a steady guide and comfort.

By the time of Esther's death (1762) Dr Burney had moved back to London,
after he had been offered the post of music-master at a girls' boarding school.
The family moved into a house in Poland Street, in a fashionable area favoured
by artists and architects, and near West End homes that could be relied upon to
seek music tuition for their children. Fanny, however, did not go to school, but
taught herself French and Italian, reading Dante, Petrarch and Voltaire in the
original. Dr Samuel Johnson lived nearby, and the family was on familiar terms
with him, but Charles Burney refused to give him permission to teach Fanny
the classical languages. This was the age in which too much learning in a woman
was considered inappropriate. All the same, Fanny persevered on her own, in

spite of her slow start, and became a voracious reader, although to begin with novels were forbidden: only improving literature such as sermons was allowed. However, she seems to have managed to smuggle in a copy of Laurence Sterne's *Sentimental Journey through France and Italy*, which she greatly enjoyed. Though it is a travelogue, not a novel, Sterne recounts his love affairs with much humour, which Fanny appreciated. Later it seems Fanny did manage to read novels, which no doubt influenced her own work.

Her father was preoccupied with study and earning a living, but another elderly friend, Samuel Crisp, took the place of godparent, tutor, and source of inspiration. He returned to London to visit Dr Burney, and stayed in the capital, becoming a much-valued mentor for Fanny, who called him 'My dear Daddy'. Dr Burney also welcomed another old friend, a widow from Lynn Regis in Norfolk, Mrs Allen, who eventually became the second Mrs Burney in 1767. Fanny did not like her, and she was never reconciled to her. However, her father's remarriage seems to have spurred Fanny to start writing — something she could do without expressing her emotions in public. These schoolgirl fictions were sadly lost: Fanny decided to destroy them on her 15th birthday after her stepmother had found her in the process of composition. She burnt them all. However, this second trauma did not stop Fanny writing.

So the creative fire was kindled. And it never burnt out. Even though she had destroyed all her poems and stories in her big bonfire, she could not give up her writing. She started a journal. In March 1768 she wrote: 'To Nobody, then, will I write my Journal! since to Nobody can I be wholly unreserved — to Nobody can I reveal every thought, every wish of my Heart, with the most unlimited confidence.'[1] Susan too began a journal: she described Fanny as having 'sense, sensibility, and bashfulness, and even a degree of prudery'. [2] Fanny continued her diary-writing for over 70 years.

During this period the family commuted between Poland Street and Lynn, where Mrs Burney still had property: so Fanny was frequently on her own in Poland Street, where she took pleasure in writing her diary in her bedroom. She seems to have been the family's prop and stay in emergencies, and they nicknamed her 'Old Lady'. At the age of 16 she longed to be in love, she told her diary, but the opportunity did not present itself. She understood too that the lives of women were often subsidiary and subordinate to those of men, which she resented. 'O how I hate this vile custom which obliges us to make slaves of ourselves!' she complained. Her stepsister Maria encouraged her defiant opinions. Between them they formulated quite a feminist agenda.

In spite of her scruples and timidity, Fanny did make an entrance into London society, accompanying her sister Hetty to a masquerade. Soon afterwards Hetty married her cousin Charles Rousseau Burney, and Fanny was thrown back on her own resources, again taking comfort from writing, and relying on Mr Crisp for support and advice. Crisp even gave her hospitality at Chessington Hall, Surrey, when she wanted to retire to write undisturbed.

Back in St Martin's Street, London, where the family had moved, they were near the actor David Garrick, who became a frequent visitor. Garrick lent the Burneys his private box in Drury Lane Theatre, and Fanny was able to see the latest productions of Shakespeare, with Garrick performing. In the meantime she was starting again her 'scribbling', taking up the stories she had begun earlier but destroyed in her big fire of 1767. One of these became her first novel, *Evelina, or The History of a Young Lady's Entrance into the World*, which was published anonymously in 1778.

The novel was still a fairly new literary form in England in this period, but had already been written by women, including Aphra Behn with *Love Letters between a Nobleman and his Sister* (1684–7). More followed in the 18th century, by Defoe, Smollett, Fielding and Sterne, and another epistolary novel, Samuel Richardson's *Pamela* (1740). Other female novelists also predated Fanny Burney: Eliza Haywood, Delarivier Manley, Sarah Scott, and Sarah Fielding (Henry's sister). The epistolary form used by Aphra Behn and by Richardson in *Pamela* was the one that Fanny adopted with *Evelina*.

This book gave Fanny an opportunity to express all her pent-up emotion, as well as to portray the richly varied society as she knew it, at all social levels. Two characters stand out. Madame Duval is the low-born woman who emigrates to Paris, and becomes a typical *nouveau riche*, with uneducated speech and embarrassing manners, who none the less finally has to be acknowledged as Evelina's grandmother. Is Fanny venting some of her pent-up feelings about her stepmother here? The other character who seems to bear a resemblance to a living person (her dear Daddy, Mr Crisp) is the elderly clergyman, the Rev Mr Villars, to whom Evelina writes her letters and tells her whole story. He can be relied upon to keep Evelina on the 'strait and narrow' path of virtue, in the face of many temptations and distractions. As for Lord Orville, whom she eventually marries: he is almost too good to be true—always courteous, polite, thoughtful, pursuing Evelina persistently through many setbacks and reversals of fortune, and finally gaining her hand.

At the same time as she was writing this book, Fanny was also acting as scribe, researcher and amanuensis to her father, Dr Charles Burney. No doubt life in London offered her many opportunities to observe society in all its richness: she visited the opera (facilitated by her father's musical connections) and the theatre, and her social circle included David Garrick, Dr Johnson, and the Thrales (Mrs Hester Thrale was a brilliant hostess to a gathering of literary friends). She wrote about Bath as well as London, and court circles as well as the middle classes and the servants. She reproduced speech at all levels in all its idiomatic idiosyncrasies.

Evelina (published when Fanny was only 26) was a great success, and so she was encouraged to go further. First she embarked on plays, but she was not successful in getting them produced. She also wrote another novel, *Cecilia, or Memoirs of an Heiress*, this time in the third person, and even longer than the three-volume *Evelina*, with five volumes and over 1,000 pages in the Oxford World Classics edition. Up till now she had remained anonymous, and *Cecilia* (1782) is acknowledged on the title page as 'by the author of Evelina'. The book gained great acclaim, with many favourable reviews. It sold out quickly and had to be reprinted.

Again the feminist streak in Fanny was given expression. The theme revolves around the fact that Cecilia, the heiress, will only inherit her estate if her husband agrees to take her surname. This of course causes endless problems, not so much with her chosen spouse as with his family. The course of true love certainly does not run smoothly, and takes us through the whole gamut of society, with some absorbing character sketches of people high and low, and some colourful conversation, with what one can only conclude are accurate representations of the vernacular. The only speeches that seem unconvincingly high-flown form the dialogue between Cecilia and her lover, Mortimer Delville. But it is a rich novel, with a changing background of both country and town, and brilliantly observed nuances of social niceties. This time, Delville is by no means perfect, and is painted in many colours. Cecilia has high moral principles, wanting to spend her considerable fortune on good works. This leads her into various dilemmas, involving the further exploration of society in all its intricacies. Fanny Burney also explores language, and is the source for many first usages quoted in the Oxford English Dictionary. Memorably, in this book she coins the phrase 'Pride and Prejudice', which of course is quoted by Jane Austen as the title of her best-known novel. 'Sense and Sensibility' is another phrase first used by Fanny in a publication: but she might well have taken it from her sister Susan, who used it in her diary.

However, work on this book was not all plain sailing. In January–March of 1781 Fanny suffered from a fever and depression, during which she had to stop work. The book was finally published in July 1782, and was an immediate success, in spite of its length. The first edition sold out quickly, and was widely discussed. All Fanny's novels are still in print, and her life story continues to fascinate.

During the writing of *Cecilia* there were other crises: the sudden death of Henry Thrale, leading to a closer friendship with his widow Hester Thrale; her sister Susan's marriage, leaving Fanny without valuable support, both emotional and as a literary critic; and further problems with her brother Charles, who had been sent down from Cambridge for stealing books, and though he now had a degree from Aberdeen, was in an unsuitable relationship with a young woman and also encumbered with debts. Charles did however embark on a programme of reform, and finally became a successful teacher.

At this point Fanny also went through an emotional experience that left her drained and depressed. She seems to have been on the brink of a serious relationship with a young clergyman, George Owen Cambridge, but owing to circumstances that are not altogether clear it all came to nothing. Her health, both mental and physical, was seriously affected. They had met at one of Elizabeth Vesey's 'Blue Stocking' parties—another interesting feature of society at the time. These were a kind of rival to traditional men's clubs, though they were not exclusively for women: men such as Horace Walpole also attended.

It was some time before Fanny's love life made any kind of progress. Further blows followed: the death of her 'dear Daddy' Samuel Crisp, and shortly afterwards, that of Samuel Johnson, affected her profoundly. Fanny went through a period of what sounds like severe depression, accompanied by anorexia. Her sisters were marrying and leaving home, and she was left with only her father and her hated stepmother for company. She resorted to religion for comfort. The emotional history of a woman susceptible to cancer seems to be evolving.

But a new door was opening: through a Mrs Delany, a grandmotherly figure whom she met in 1783, she was invited to join the royal household of George III as Second Keeper of the Robes to Queen Charlotte. This was an invitation she could not refuse, in spite of her serious misgivings. Her father had been hoping for an appointment as Master of the King's Band, but instead Fanny had been offered a post that she felt she must accept, partly to ameliorate her father's position at court. But for Fanny it meant virtual incarceration, away from all her friends, and obliged to perform trivial tasks for the Queen—helping to dress her, starting at six in the morning and ending only at midnight. Her duties actually amounted to very little, and Fanny spent a good deal of time simply hanging about. Her depression returned.

Her immediate superior at court was Juliana Schwellenberg (who had accompanied Queen Charlotte from Germany), and their antipathy was mutual. Fanny's transcribing of her speech in her diary is hilarious: as usual, Fanny's ear for accent and dialogue is acute. Fanny spent five years in her role as the Queen's wardrobe mistress, never being able to call her time her own, since she had to be constantly available at the summons of a bell to respond to her royal mistress's demands. However, she recorded much in her journal, which paints a fascinating picture of life at court.

Mrs Delany, who had introduced Fanny to the royal family, died in 1788; this was another blow, since she had been a wonderful friend to Fanny, who was able to escape to her house in Windsor after dinner at court, for stimulating conversation. Fanny began writing a tragedy, to while away the hours not on active duty. She continued to write her journal, which she sent in instalments to her sister Susan.

A serious problem now arose: the King's mental illness, which started in 1788. His physicians had no idea how to treat him, and the Queen was distraught, which meant that Fanny entered a new phase of intimacy with her, as she was now treated as a confidante. She observed strict confidentiality, entrusting nothing to her diary about the King's illness. It lasted for five months, and was acutely distressing to all who witnessed it. He became dangerous and violent.

Fanny herself saw the first signs of the King's recovery when she encountered him unexpectedly in Kew Palace Gardens: he saw her and chased after her: she ran away, terrified, but finally had to face him, upon which he gave her an embrace, kissing her on the cheek. He proceeded to have a perfectly lucid conversation with her, enquiring about her novel-writing and her father's music, and then discussing the history of music, and his favourite composer, Handel.

During the King's illness the court had resided at Kew, but on his recovery he returned to Windsor, with much rejoicing. Meanwhile Fanny had been attracted by Colonel Digby, who had official business with the court, and spent long hours with Fanny in her bedroom, since he had no apartment of his own in the palace. However, he finally married one of the maids of honour, and Fanny, now 39, was once more bitterly disappointed. Still incarcerated in the palace, with no one for company except the insufferable Madame Schwellenberg, she was broken in spirit and in poor health. Her life had become intolerable, and she confessed to her father that she must escape the court. In October 1790 she finally asked the Queen for permission to resign. This was granted, and Fanny received a pension of £100 a year for the rest of her life.

On her release she was taken under the wing of Mrs Anna Ord, one of the original 'Blue Stockings'. On their journey to Winchester they encountered a party of aristocrats, refugees from the 1789 Revolution in France. Some of them ended up renting Juniper Hall, which was at the foot of Box Hill in Surrey, near where Fanny's sister Susan was living. In 1791 Susan encountered some of these *émigrés*, including General d'Arblay, who impressed her with his upper-class manners and warm personality. He had been a lifelong soldier, but was also a poet and musician: he played the mandolin and was a voracious reader. He had been a frequent visitor to Susan and her family, before Fanny herself met him while staying with Susan. She was immediately attracted to him, and asked her father's permission to extend her stay with her sister. D'Arblay offered to give her French lessons, and this was the cover for their deepening friendship. They were in fact mutual language tutors, and as their fluency in each other's languages grew, so did their love for each other. This time Fanny really had found her ideal husband.

But there were obstacles: Fanny's father would not approve of a man who was Catholic, French, and penniless (though he had property in France). D'Arblay was also a friend of the Comte de Narbonne, a lover of the notorious Madame de Staël, and one of the group of French *émigrés* living in Juniper Hall. Finally Fanny had to return to her father in London, but d'Arblay set off to walk the 18 miles to bring her a rose tree. He wooed her with more roses, and visits to Chelsea (when Dr Burney remained in his room and refused to see him), and they were finally married in

Mickleham Church, near her sister Susan's cottage, on 28th July 1793, followed by a Roman Catholic celebration on 30th July in London. Fanny was already 41.

D'Arblay had no income, and Fanny's court pension of £100 was hardly enough for one gentlewoman to live on, let alone a married couple. So Fanny turned again to her writing. Her husband's only chance of preferment would be in France, and for now this was out of the question: war with France had started in 1793. Meanwhile they rented a cottage in Great Bookham, where d'Arblay turned amateur gardener and Fanny learned domestic skills for the first time in her life.

Fanny first produced a pamphlet designed to raise money for the French refugees, then reverted to her play-writing (though her blank verse tragedy *Edwy and Elgiva* was a disastrous flop) and finally embarked on a new novel, *Camilla*, which was finally published, again anonymously, with 'by the author of *Evelina* and *Cecilia*' on the title page. The earnings from this enabled them to build their own home, on land nearby that had been given to them, and they called it Camilla Cottage. (They moved in 1797.) Even more importantly, at the age of 42, in 1794, she gave birth to her son, named Alexander (Alex). He seemed highly intelligent from infancy, and gave his parents great delight. At the age of only three he was presented at court.

Late child-bearing is a well-known risk factor for breast cancer, and Fanny's life up to this point, even though she was now in a loving relationship with d'Arblay, had been full of trauma: bereavements, failed relationships, and serious depression. But her marriage to d'Arblay seems to have been very happy, in spite of their financial straits, and d'Arblay's difficulties in finding suitable employment in England. It was providential that Fanny could rely on her writing to bring in a modest income, and her third novel, *Camilla,* benefited from her earlier writing experience and also her improved business sense: this time she made sure of commercial success by selling her manuscript to the highest bidder, using her brother Charles as agent. They decided to market the work by subscription of one guinea, and Fanny gave herself a deadline for completion: 1st July 1796. This was advertised in the *Morning Chronicle* for 7th July 1795, so Fanny could not afford to hang about. Her husband helped with transcribing the text, and finally making a fair copy after Fanny's many revisions. Through the agency of Charles she sold the copyright for £1,000 (worth almost £150,000 today) to Payne, Cadell and Davies.

Reviews were mixed. Some found it too long, though it was no longer than *Cecilia* (perhaps tastes were changing). But financially it was a success, making about £2,000 in all for its needy family, and almost selling out the first edition within three months. After much negotiation, and many corrections and revisions, a second edition was finally published in 1802, but by this time the d'Arblays were in France, and cut off from England owing to the resumption of hostilities.

Grief struck the Burney family again: Elizabeth Burney, Fanny's stepmother, died in October 1796. Though Fanny had never liked her, it had a devastating effect on her father, whom she tried to help and console, visiting Chelsea for a fortnight while d'Arblay and their child stayed in Camilla Cottage. Fanny was to suffer a further setback with the illness and death of her dear sister Susan, who had been compelled to accompany her husband to his home country, Ireland. The marriage had not gone well: Major Phillips turned out to be a gambler, womanizer, and bully, and while in Ireland Susan's health deteriorated rapidly. She finally died on her way back to England on 6th January 1800. Susan had not only been Fanny's confidante, but also her valued literary critic. Fanny was devastated, and kept 6th January as a special memorial day for the rest of her life.

Recovery from grief was slow, but Fanny once more resumed her writing. Meanwhile d'Arblay was thinking of returning to France, since although France and England were still at war, internally France was more stable, and Napoleon was now First Consul. D'Arblay hoped to steady the family's finances by making something of his estate in Joigny. This idea proved fruitless. However, in 1801 d'Arblay was exploring the possibility of military service with Napoleon, or at least a military pension. In early 1802 d'Arblay returned to France, and though he could not secure a suitable military appointment, in April 1802 he persuaded Fanny to join him, bringing Alex with her. In March 1802 the Peace of Amiens had been declared: England and France were no longer at war. Cultural life in Paris resumed, and Fanny was launched into a whirl of social engagements. Their apartment up three flights of stairs in the Rue de Miroménil was small, but central, and they were soon meeting again their *émigré* friends from Juniper Hall, including Narbonne.

D'Arblay was seen by Fanny in a new light, as he was greeted by many of his old friends and companions. Fanny herself was already known in Paris for her second novel, *Cecilia,* which had been translated into French and published in 1783. However, this intense metropolitan episode was not to last: the family left Paris to stay in Joigny, where d'Arblay had property. Here he had many friends and relations, and Fanny had to meet them all, which she found tiring. They returned to Paris, but this time bought a house in Passy, outside the city, with the proceeds from selling property in Joigny. In 1803 d'Arblay had secured a small military pension, and achieved the rank of Adjutant-Général in retirement. However, Napoleon now declared war on Britain, and for Fanny all hopes of returning to England were dashed. Correspondence was censored, and she felt despairingly cut off from her family. Also, she lost access to her royal pension, so her husband had to seek employment to balance the books. He secured a low-paid civil service job, which meant that the family had to move back into the city. Fanny devoted herself to caring for Alex, who was growing wild and rebellious. She also made a start on a new novel.

However, her right breast became lumpy and painful. After months during which the problem increased, she was finally advised to consult Baron

Dominique-Jean Larrey, who was a renowned army surgeon, used to battlefield amputations, which he carried out at an astounding rate. He undertook to perform a mastectomy, which was done at her home on 30th September 1811, without anaesthetic, though she was allowed a wine cordial. Fanny's own account of this operation is extremely long and detailed. It was finally sent to her sister, Esther Burney (Hetty).

> I rang for my Maid & Nurses, — but before I could speak to them, my room, without previous message, was entered by 7 Men in black, Dr. Larry, M. Dubois, Dr. Moreau, Dr. Aumont, Dr. Ribe, & a pupil of Dr. Larry, & another of M. Dubois. I was now awakened from my stupor — & by a sort of indignation — Why so many? & without leave? — but I could not utter a syllable. M. Dubois acted as Commander in Chief. Dr. Larry kept out of sight; M. Dubois ordered a Bedstead into the middle of the room. Astonished, I turned to Dr. Larry, who had promised that an Arm Chair would suffice; but he hung his head, & would not look at me.[3]

Fanny continues to describe the operation in all its gory detail. It is a *tour de force*.

> M. Dubois placed me upon the Mattress, & spread a cambric handkerchief upon my face. It was transparent, however, & I saw, through it, that the Bedstead was instantly surrounded by the 7 men & my nurse. I refused to be held; but when, Bright through the cambric, I saw the glitter of polished Steel — I closed my Eyes. I would not trust to convulsive fear the sight of the terrible incision.

The description continues, with its account of excruciating pain, followed by the ritual of dressing the wound, carrying the patient to her bed for rest and recovery.

> This removal made me open my Eyes — & I then saw my good Dr. Larry, pale nearly as myself, his face streaked with blood, & its expression depicting grief, apprehension, & almost horrour.

D'Arblay himself adds a note to Fanny's account at this point, though it is obviously written later, with the news: 'Thank Heaven! She is now surprisingly well, & in good spirits, & we hope to have many many still happy days.'

Some writers have queried whether Fanny's problem was in fact cancer, since it is unusual for breast cancer to be accompanied by pain. But it is not unheard of, and the medical report of the operation, completed by Baron Larrey's 'Chief Pupil', is unequivocal. His note of 1st October 1811 says:

> Madame D'arblay a subi hier à 3 heures ¾ L'extirpation d'une tumeur Cancéreuse du Volume du poing et adhérente au muscle grand Pectorale et Développée dans le sein droit. L'opération faite par Mr Le Baron Larrey, assisté du Professeur Dubois & des Docteurs Moreau, Ribes, (Hereau) & Aumont, a été très douloureuse & supportée avec un grand Courage.[4]

Not much doubt here about it being a cancerous tumour, and there were plenty of expert witnesses. It was obviously huge: the size of a fist! But Fanny seems to have recovered remarkably quickly from her ordeal. It is not stated whether or not the lymph nodes were involved. She was to live another 29 years.

So how did she survive such an obviously overwhelming experience? Perhaps one secret was her extraordinary ability to describe it in such powerful detail. She had to look after her young son and contribute to the family income, but did not need to repress the pain of her trauma.

When a peace treaty was signed between France and Britain on 24th March 1812, this gave Fanny the opportunity to return home: she wanted to see her father, now 85, and take Alex to explore further education in England, thus avoiding conscription into the French army. She left her husband behind in France: d'Arblay did not wish to risk his job. Fanny was still having difficulty with writing, as her right arm and shoulder had been badly affected by the surgery, but Alex helped out. It is not clear from Baron Larrey's pupil's record whether or not he had removed lymph nodes from her armpit, but if so, this would have affected her arm.

Their journey to England was nothing if not eventful: in fact the ship they travelled on was destined for America, and the diversion via Deal, where they landed, was providential. Finally Fanny was able to return to Chelsea, and meet her father again. He was in poor health. She was anxious too to catch up with family news, especially with the children of her sister Susan. Fanny reported back to her husband in France all the gossip; during their ten years away, there had been very limited opportunity for correspondence owing to the war situation and the interception of letters.

Her sister Charlotte's children included two girls, who took advantage of the new educational opportunities offered to females, learning both modern and ancient languages, and though they could not study at university nevertheless explored academic interests. Fanny herself was now occupied in securing a university education for Alex. Her brother Charles (now vicar of St Paul's, Deptford, and Chaplain to George III) helped with organizing tuition, and found him a scholarship at Gonville & Caius College, Cambridge, where he started in October 1813.

Fanny's own finances were however in disarray, and she devoted all her spare time to finishing her new novel, *The Wanderer, or Female Difficulties*. By March 1813 she embarked on negotiating terms, once again using Charles as her agent. A contract was finally agreed with Longman & Co., and the book was published in March 1814. *The Wanderer* does not deal directly with Paris or the French Revolution, though the wanderer herself is a refugee from France. It is set in Regency England, focusing on the difficulties of being female. Again Fanny's feminist agenda is clear. *The Wanderer* is even longer than *Cecilia*, and according to some is 'her richest and most rewarding book'.[5] Again, the title page states that it is 'by the author of *Evelina; Cecilia;* and *Camilla*', but it also has a long Foreword to Doctor Burney, which she signs 'F. B. d'Arblay': no anonymity here.

The Wanderer of the title is a mysterious woman seeking refuge from France, who manages to get aboard a boat carrying *émigrés*, but is heavily disguised to start with, and refuses to give her name or recount her history. She is obviously of good birth, even though she loses her purse and has no money, and is dependent on charity for survival. Slowly however she makes her way. Luckily she is a talented harpist, and she survives by giving music lessons.

Feminism is again an interesting theme: its most vehement statement is not in fact made by the Wanderer herself, but by her rival in love, Elinor, who talks of her 'revolutionary ideas', to which she owes 'the precious privilege, so shamefully new to mankind, of daring to think for myself'.[6] It seems as if Fanny does not dare to put the most outrageous statement of feminism in the mouth of her heroine (and at that time was not likely to recognize the sexism in the word 'mankind'): but feminism is all the same clearly part of her agenda.

Talk of feminism cannot escape mention of Mary Wollstonecraft, who in 1782 published *A Vindication of the Rights of Woman*. Mary too was a member of the Dr Johnson circle, and must surely have read Fanny's novels: Fanny probably reciprocated. She also spent some time in France during this period, arriving in 1792, and even wrote a history of the early French Revolution, published in 1794. She was seven years younger than Fanny, but packed a great deal into her short life, dying soon after her second childbirth in 1797 at the age of only 38.

The first edition of *The Wanderer* sold out quickly, but half the second edition did not sell, and it was unfavourably reviewed by Macaulay and Hazlitt, among others. It did not receive its deserved critical acclaim until the feminist revival of the 1970s. But Fanny had other things to worry about: she had not heard from her husband, trapped in Paris, which was about to be besieged by Russia and Prussia. However, Napoleon capitulated, the Russian Emperor entered the capital, and peace was concluded. The Bourbons were restored to the French throne, and Louis XVIII, brother of the beheaded King, took his place. He was crowned on 3rd May 1814.

In the meantime Fanny's father lay dying, with Fanny at his bedside. He left her £1,000 in his will. Fanny felt obliged to see to her father's affairs, staying in London, while M. d'Arblay dashed over from Paris to be with her, since the war was over. However, he only stayed a month before returning to France to accept a post in Louis XVIII's bodyguard, leaving Fanny to cope with the problem that they were about to lose Camilla Cottage, owing to an obscure legal entanglement. She was thus left without a home she could call her own, with only a relatively small amount for recompense. She wanted to stay in England, to keep an eye on Alex, who was studying at Cambridge. But her husband could not understand: in his view, a military career in France would be preferable to whatever England could offer Alex. However, Alex refused to leave Cambridge, and in the end only Fanny accompanied d'Arblay back to France.

The stay in France started badly: d'Arblay was involved in a near-fatal accident, taking months to recover. Back in Paris, the d'Arblays spent a quiet winter, but Napoleon had now escaped from exile in Elba, and by mid-March was at the gates of Paris with his troops. D'Arblay told Fanny that she must leave Paris, so she made her way to Brussels, escaping confusion in France, and finally her husband caught up with her. They stayed there, where the Duke of Wellington was also staying and preparing for the battle of Waterloo. On 30th May war was declared against Napoleon by the allied European forces, but by this time d'Arblay was elsewhere and Fanny could not contact him.

The next days were spent in agonies of uncertainty, but finally intelligence of Wellington's victory over Napoleon trickled through. Fanny wrote to her husband, now in Trèves, with the news, but he had yet another serious accident, when he was kicked by a horse, so Fanny set off on a perilous journey to join him. She found him in very poor health, and it took another month before he was fit to travel. Finally they made it back to Paris, and after a period of convalescence d'Arblay agreed that his military career was over. They returned to England in October 1815.

The d'Arblays were back in London, and M. d'Arblay now had the title of 'Comte', but he was retired from the army, and still limping after his accident. They went to Bath to try the waters. Living modestly, they also attended the theatre, seeing Edmund Kean as Hamlet, and even went to a ball. Fanny renewed her acquaintance with Mrs Thrale, now Thrale-Piozzi. D'Arblay returned to Paris to settle his affairs, while Fanny stayed in Bath to make sure that Alex stuck to his studies. They then went to Ilfracombe, where Alex was engaged on a vacation reading party. D'Arblay finally returned from France to join them, though he was now in poor health; when he was finally diagnosed with cancer of the rectum, it was too advanced for surgery. However, Alex had achieved a first-class degree in mathematics, and was 10th in the list of 28 Wranglers. The following March he was elected a Fellow of Christ's College. But by April his father was seriously ill, and he died on 3rd May 1818. He was buried in Bath on 9th May. He was 65, and his wife wrote the words for a memorial stone erected on the wall of St Swithin's Church, Walcot Street.

After a period of intense grief Fanny returned to London, and Alex to Cambridge, leaving Fanny alone in Bolton Street, off Piccadilly. She resumed daily walks in Green Park and Hyde Park: even now she somehow knew how to keep healthy. She also decided to edit her father's papers, with a view to making some money. In fact she found little worth preserving, and instead wrote her own biography of her father. It took her twelve years, and her *Memoirs of Doctor Burney* was finally published in November 1832. Favourable reviews followed, though it was later attacked by John Croker, who slated it in the *Quarterly Review,* criticizing the fact that Fanny had dispensed with so much of her father's own material.

However, Fanny was more worried now about Alex, who though ordained, as was required of a Cambridge don, took little interest in his students, and led a wandering life during vacations. He accepted a living in Camden, but was inconsistent and unreliable in serving his parishioners. At last Alex found a suitable partner, but could not marry her for lack of funds. Finally he achieved a satisfactory living in Holborn, but caught a severe chill while taking a service in a cold chapel, and died of influenza. Mary Ann Smith, the fiancée he never married, took care of Fanny, who was now 84, deaf and with cataracts in both eyes. Her only living sibling was now her younger sister Charlotte, whom she visited for a month in Brighton. Charlotte too died in 1838, and Fanny was left on her own. But she retained her lively outlook, with regular visits from her old friend George Owen Cambridge, now Archdeacon, and the poet Samuel Rogers.

Her health was deteriorating, but she never lost her mental faculties. She died on 6th January 1840, aged 87, on the anniversary of her dear sister Susan's death, and was buried in Bath next to her husband and son. Fanny's works include not just her four lengthy novels, but also the *Diary and Letters of Madame d'Arblay*, which offer a fascinating historical document of a significant period in European as well as English history. Even more important for the theme of this book, her creative fire was never foiled, and she lived for over 29 years after her mastectomy.

Select Bibliography

Frances Burney	*Evelina, or The History of a Young Lady's Entrance into the World,* ed. Margaret Anne Doody (Penguin Classics, London,1994)
Frances Burney	*Cecilia, or Memoirs of an Heiress*, ed. Peter Sabor and Margaret Anne Doody (Oxford World's Classics: Oxford University Press, Oxford,1988)
Frances Burney	*Camilla, or A Picture of Youth*, ed. Edward A. Bloom and Lillian D. Bloom (Oxford World's Classics, Oxford University Press, Oxford, 1972)
Frances Burney	*The Wanderer or Female Difficulties*, ed. Margaret Anne Doody, Robert L. Mack, and Peter Sabor (Oxford World's Classics: Oxford University Press, Oxford, 1991)
Kate Chisholm	*Fanny Burney: her life* (Chatto & Windus, London, 1998; Vintage, London, 1999)
Claire Harman	*Fanny Burney: a biography* (HarperCollins, London, 2000)

J. Hemlow *et al.* (eds)	*The Journals and Letters of Fanny Burney (Madame d'Arblay), 1791–1840* (12 vols, Oxford University Press, Oxford, 1972–84)
Janice Farrar Thaddeus	*Frances Burney: a Literary Life* (St Martin's Press Inc., London, 2000)
Mary Wollstonecraft	*A Vindication of the Rights of Woman* (together with John Stuart Mill: *On the Subjection of Women*) (Everyman's Library, Dent, London, 1929)

Notes

1. quoted in Chisholm, p. 25.
2. *ibid.*, p. 26.
3. Hemlow *et al.* (eds), 30th September 1811, p. 610.
4. *ibid.*, p. 616. 'Madam d'Arblay underwent yesterday at 3.45 the excision of a tumour the size of a fist and adhering to the great pectoral muscle, on the right breast. The operation performed by Baron Larrey, assisted by Professor Dubois and Doctors Moreau, Ribes, (Hereau) and Aumont, was very painful and undergone with great courage.'
5. Chisholm, p. 230.
6. Burney, *The Wanderer,* p. 173.

Christina Rossetti

CHRISTINA ROSSETTI WAS THE FOURTH AND youngest child of an Italian refugee, Gabriele Rossetti, who had fled his homeland, the Kingdom of Naples, and Frances Polidori, also of Italian descent, though her father had settled in Britain earlier, and had an English wife. Gabriele was 43 and Frances 26 when they married. It is thought that Gabriele may well have left behind a wife and child when he fled Italy, but this was not spoken of in England. The four children of Gabriele and Frances followed in swift succession, after which no more children appeared. All the children were baptized into the Church of England, though their father was nominally a Catholic. Christina Georgina was born on 5th December 1830, after Maria, Dante Gabriel, and William.

Christina Georgina Rossetti
from a tinted crayon drawing by Dante Rossetti 1877

From the nursery Christina loved rhyming, and she had a happy childhood, spent partly in London, where her father obtained a post as Professor of Italian at King's College. He did a great deal of peripatetic teaching and research, as the Chair was not remunerated. Her maternal grandfather, Gaetano Polidori, was also a teacher and translator, and the family spent holidays at his home in Holmer Green, on the edge of the Chilterns, where outdoor activities gave Christina much enjoyment. The family was bilingual.

Christina learnt her letters at home with her mother, who saw to domestic duties and finances. Moral teaching was also her province: obedience, perseverance and self-control were guiding principles. She went away from time to time to look after her own mother, 'Granny Pierce'. She was also a generous dispenser of aid and gifts to refugees. Altogether Christina had very firm moral guidance, but she was a lively child, and very pretty, unlike her elder sister Maria. She was also clever and industrious, and together with Maria defied the contemporary reluctance to allow girls to engage in serious study.

Christina started writing poetry when she was 11, with a poem to her mother on her birthday. Others followed regularly. However, the family was now suffering from the decline of Gabriele's academic career: Italian was now not so popular a study as German, owing to the young Queen Victoria's marriage to a German prince. His commentary on Dante's *Inferno* found scant favour, and his professional competence and even mental health were called into question. His physical health and eyesight also deteriorated, and finally he had to give up teaching and was confined to the house.

At this point his wife had to balance the books by going out to work as a governess. Maria too worked as a governess, leaving Christina, now 13, at home to look after her father. She had to act as his amanuensis, as his sight was now very poor, and no doubt also took on various domestic tasks, replacing her mother. Poetry provided an emotional outlet, and in 1844 she composed her first long poem, 'The Water Spirit's Song'. She also wrote in Italian.

There is a suspicion that Christina was forced to replace her mother in another manner. Her biographer writes: 'Perhaps, too, her father made excessive demands, confusing Christina's companionate role with that of his absent wife... behaviour that in a previously loved and admired father would be truly pitiable but also frightening to his bewildered daughter.'[1] If Christina's father made sexual advances to her, it would account for her nervous breakdown, which led to self-harm (cutting her arm with a pair of scissors) and serious depression.

When Christina was on the verge of puberty, she seems to have changed from a bright, lively girl with a genuine talent for writing verse to a solitary, inward-looking young woman. This adolescent trauma may well have accounted for her subsequent health history and personality. In those days telling anyone about her problems with her father would have been unthinkable—indeed even in the 21st century many women try to bury such memories, and when they do tell them, they are not always believed. But it seems that the evidence is there in her poetry, in particular 'Hope in Grief', written when she was nearly 15 (on 3rd December 1845), but unpublished:

> *When we find ourselves betrayed,*
> *When we find ourselves forsaken,*
> *By those for whom we would have laid*
> *Our young lives down, nor wished to waken...*
> *What though we should be deceived*
> *By the friend that we love best?...*[2]

Christina also gave up many pleasures such as going to plays and operas, and even playing chess (which she was used to doing with her father). Her life had taken a very sad downward turn, and her whole personality changed.

During this period she was also influenced by the emerging Tractarian movement towards Catholicism in the Anglican Church, and attended Christ Church, Albany

Street, which was the centre of Anglo-Catholicism, of which John Henry Newman was the leading light. Christina became more pious, and wrote many religious poems. The writing of poetry was deemed an acceptable pursuit for young ladies, who otherwise were not allowed many ambitions, and for whom work as a governess was about the only profession available.

Preparation for confirmation in this environment offered her the possibility of confession, of which she seems to have taken advantage. She wrote in 'Divine and Human Pleading' (March 1846):

Weeping I sought the Lord of life,
Bowed with my shame and sin;
And thereunto my wondering heart
Love's searching fire came in.[3]

It is not at all uncommon that girls who have been abused blame themselves for it, as any psychotherapist will testify. If we are right in attributing her breakdown to her father's inappropriate behaviour, it is unsurprising that Christina should blame herself. However, she may have found some relief from confession and absolution. And life was not entirely dark. Later in 1846 she benefited from a seaside holiday in Folkestone, and took great delight in rock pools, seaweed, pebbles, starfish, and watching the children playing. She wrote more poems, and her grandfather, Gaetano Polidori, published a collection of them titled *Verses* (1847), when Christina was only 16. Another seaside holiday came the following year, and many more poems. However, the theme of inner tragedy continued.

A shrinking in the memory
From some forgotten harm
'The Last Hope' (1847) [4]

A literary club was proposed by a nucleus of young men in London, including Christina's brother Dante Gabriel, but Christina herself declined to join, or even to have her poems read there by her brother. She abhorred immodesty, and a mixed group would have been too much for her. But she continued to write.

Dante Gabriel was also occupied with another artistic grouping, the Pre-Raphaelite Brotherhood (PRB), which aimed to cut out the influence of Raphael and revert to early Flemish and Italian artists for inspiration. The group included Dante Gabriel and William Rossetti, Holman Hunt, and John Millais. Their ambitions were literary as well as artistic, and Christina was drawn in as a poet, despite her earlier shyness, resulting in the publication in 1848 of two of her poems ('Death's Chill Between' and 'Heart's Chill Between') in the *Athenaeum,* an important literary weekly, when she was only 17.

James Collinson, a member of the PRB, who had exhibited at the Royal Academy in 1847, and attended the same church as Christina, was invited to the Rossetti household. However, at this point he decided to go over to the Roman

Catholic Church, so his proposal of marriage to Christina, still under age at 17, presented two obstacles. A third was that she was not in love with him. But when he later re-converted to Anglicanism she decided to accept him after all.

Christina had been modelling for her brother Dante Gabriel, and also sat for James, who painted her portrait, which he took home to Mansfield to show his parents, accompanied by Christina's brother William. In his absence Christina wrote one of her most famous poems (December 1848):

When I am dead, my dearest,
Sing no sad songs for me;
Plant thou no roses at my head,
Nor shady cypress tree...[5]

She spent a month with the Collinson family (in James' absence: he was painting on the Isle of Wight), and back in London her feelings for James seem to have deepened, and her association with the PRB also increased. This now inaugurated a magazine, *The Germ*, which provided a new vehicle for Christina's own poems as well as those of her male contemporaries, though it only survived for four issues. Then, in 1851 Christina's fiancé James reverted to Roman Catholicism. This broke her heart, and the engagement was broken off too. At the age of 21, after already making something of an emotional pilgrimage, she could not follow James into Catholicism, so she had to abandon him, and what followed was a severe setback psychologically, leading also to physical disorders such as migraine.

Still only 21, Christina was crushed and bruised. It must have been mortifying to have embarked somewhat reluctantly on her emotional journey towards marriage with James, only to see him move back to Catholicism, which might have felt like a rejection. It was doubly distressing since she had so recently recovered from her adolescent breakdown, only to be set back emotionally once again. Religion provided some comfort, and in poetry (largely unpublished) she was able to express her innermost feelings without risk of public disclosure.

A new literary venture was a feminine magazine, *The Bouquet from Marylebone Gardens*, with contributors assuming the names of flowers. Later, men joined in, using the names of vegetables. Christina contributed poems in Italian under the name Calta (Italian for 'marigold'), and also prose, in the form of an epistolary novel. Like *The Germ,* the *Bouquet* did not last long. Christina's next publication was *Nick,* a fairy tale in which she could sublimate her repressed anger.

She showed interest all her life in liberal if not socialist campaigns, helping the poor and needy through Church philanthropy, and attracted to the anti-slavery movement. She was also an anti-vivisectionist, and something of a feminist, though her support for female suffrage was inconsistent and equivocal. At one point she was arguing for votes for women and even for women MPs, but at another she actually signed the anti-women's suffrage petition organized by Mary Ward.

Home life changed abruptly when Christina's mother, Frances, decided to give up teaching in London and moved to Frome in Somerset, where she set up a new school. The school opened, but soon afterwards Frances had to return to her mother's deathbed. Further bereavements followed: Grandpapa Gaetano Polidori died after a stroke, much to Christina's distress, and soon after, her own father—far less lamented than Grandpapa. The Pre-Raphaelite Brotherhood had also ended, and the school in Frome was closed.

But there were new stimuli. Christina's next philanthropic move was to volunteer to nurse wounded soldiers in the Crimea, following Florence Nightingale. In fact she was rejected (possibly as too young and inexperienced), though her Aunt Eliza Polidori did serve as a nurse, in charge of stores at the Barrack Hospital. At home, Maria and Christina took over her parish duties. But Christina was once again subject to fits of depression, leading also to physical illness. She became an invalid and a recluse.

The poetic muse was not stifled, however, and the feminist agenda was given further expression in her unpublished poem 'From the Antique' (1863):

It's a weary life, it is; she said:—
Doubly blank is a woman's lot:
I wish and I wish I were a man;
Or, better than any being, were not.[6]

Christina's struggle with feminist ideas lasted all her life. At this period she greatly admired Elizabeth Barrett Browning, who seemed to have achieved feminine fulfilment in her marriage to Robert, while also writing brilliantly, and in no way in his shadow.

Christina herself, while unfulfilled emotionally, was nevertheless coming into full fruition poetically. She became adventurous, using unconventional verse forms. Again her inner struggles find expression:

I wish it were over, the terrible pain,
Pang after pang again and again:
First the shattering ruining blow,
Then the probing steady and slow…
'Introspective' (1857) [7]

Her poem 'In the Round Tower at Jhansi' (1857), though based on false press accounts of an assault by Indian troops on a British military station, was very powerful, and brought her acclaim. Further poems followed about keeping secrets, a recurrent theme.

While Christina's career as a poet progressed apace, her erstwhile fiancé James Collinson, now aged 32, married Eliza Wheeler, aged 40, who was also a Catholic, and it seems of independent means. If Christina still had hopes of marrying him, they were now at an end.

John Brett was the next person to be taken with Christina. He was a Pre-Raphaelite painter, a disciple of Ruskin; he lived near the Rossettis, was a little younger than Christina, and painted a portrait of her. It is not at all clear whether or not he actually proposed, and if he did, why Christina refused him, but there was certainly an attraction. Her poem 'I never said I loved you, John' (March 1860) adds to the mystery.

But during this period she also experienced deep depression and spiritual desolation. Her poem: 'Sorrow not as those who have no hope' (November 1858) is summed up by the lines:

She measured measureless sorrow towards its length
And breadth, and depth, and height... [8]

Christina was now a successful poet, but she sought other ways of making the world a better place, and became a volunteer at a 'penitentiary' for 'fallen' women. Prostitution was rife in Victorian London: women could earn much more in this way than by 'honest' work. The St Mary Magdalene home in Highgate, run by the Anglican Church, aimed to reform penitent prostitutes and train them for domestic service. From 1859 Christina was spending long periods helping with this work, as 'Sister Christina'. (Ironically, during the same period her brother Dante Gabriel was consorting with prostitutes, using one Fanny Cornforth as a model for his painting.) Christina stayed as a volunteer for several years, even being asked to be Lady Principal (a post she declined). She also did a good deal of fundraising for the home. The stories told by women at this institution remained confidential, but nonetheless influenced her writing.

Arising out of her work at the penitentiary, it would seem, came her longest and most famous poem, *Goblin Market* (1862), with its theme of forbidden fruit. The devilish goblin merchants tempt two sisters, Laura and Lizzie, with luscious fruit: 'Come buy, come buy!' Laura gives way, and then falls seriously ill. Lizzie rescues her by embarking on a perilous journey to find the goblin men and bringing back juices to heal her. The message is obvious: steer clear of temptation. But in many ways it is erotic, and even incestuous, as when Lizzie returns from her own adventure with the goblins:

Did you miss me?
Come and kiss me.
Never mind my bruises,
Hug me, kiss me, suck my juices
Squeezed from goblin fruits for you,
Goblin pulp and goblin dew.
Eat me, drink me, love me;
Laura, make much of me:
For your sake I have braved the glen
And had to do with goblin merchant men. [9]

Goblin Market (published in 1862) was an instant success, receiving excellent reviews, and bringing Christina widespread fame. She was now 31. But another nervous illness followed: perhaps, as a woman in a male-dominated world, she felt she had not deserved to succeed.

She was also upset by the death of her sister-in-law Lizzie (Dante Gabriel's wife), from an overdose of laudanum, which was not classed as suicide. However, a new love interest emerged: Charles Cayley, a pupil of her father's, a scholarly recluse, was attracted to Christina and she to him.

It seems that Christina's good causes included a feeling for ecological justice, as in her unpublished poem 'To what purpose is this waste?' (1853):

> The tiniest living thing
> That soars on feathered wing,
> Or crawls among the long grass out of sight
> To its appointed portion of delight
> As any King.
> Why should we grudge a hidden water stream
> To birds and squirrels while we have enough?[10]

(Much later, in 1876, she signed a petition against the destruction of part of the New Forest.) Further feminist campaigning followed, with an anthology designed to support the Lancashire textile workers. Charles Cayley was suggested by Christina as a contributor. He and Christina seem to have conducted their relationship largely through poetry, in which Christina's contribution was certainly superior. But apparently poetry was its only medium, and the two shy people never really got together. Finally in August 1866 Cayley asked Christina to marry him, but she refused. Finance may have been an issue, and religion another. It seems that Cayley was not a sufficiently orthodox Christian to meet Christina's demanding standard. However, she continued to see him at intervals at least until 1881, and in 1883 he bequeathed to her his 'best writing desk' in his will. He died shortly afterwards, and Christina was his literary executor.

The Rev Charles Dodgson ('Lewis Carroll'), author of *Alice in Wonderland,* was a visitor to the Rossetti household, and took photographs of the family. Another friend was Jean Ingelow, who was something of a literary rival. Christina was becoming well known in literary circles.

By 1871 Christina (now aged 41) was living in Euston Square with her family, consisting of her brother William, working for the Inland Revenue, her sister Maria, who was teaching languages, her mother, aunt Eliza, aunt Charlotte, and three servants. Christina then had a sudden onset of a mysterious illness that eminent physicians such as Dr Jenner found difficult to diagnose. She had a high fever, tremor, and muscle weakness. The fever subsided but the weakness did not, and she developed a mouth abscess and a swollen throat. She lost her hair, her eyes protruded, and her head ached. Finally Graves' disease, a thyroid disorder, was diagnosed. Her appearance was changed, and she looked much older as a result. She went into remission, but relapsed at the same time as her brother Dante Gabriel was struck by severe paranoid schizophrenia, hearing voices and unable to sleep.

William had to take on a great deal of responsibility as a result, for both his sister Christina and his brother. Slowly Christina recovered, though her looks did not. We now know that hypothyroidism (leading to Graves' disease) is a risk factor for breast cancer, which finally proved fatal for Christina. In the meantime however her creativity continued.

Her domestic life changed, with William's marriage to Lucy Brown, and Maria's entry to the All Saints Sisterhood as a nun. With Maria absent, and often unable to attend church herself owing to her illness, Christina embarked on a pious undertaking to write a book of devotions, *Annus Domini*, with prayers for each day of the year. The metaphysical poet John Donne, and Lancelot Andrewes (with his book of daily prayers, the *Preces Privatae*), were probably influences here. But the prayers were addressed not to God the Father but to God the Son: was she unable to bring herself to use the word 'Father' because of her adolescent experience with her own father? That her prayer book was actually published illustrates again a feminist streak in Christina: though modest in matters religious, she was not afraid of putting out a devotional volume, even in competition with Victorian clergy, who were invariably male. A further publication was *Speaking Likenesses* (1874), which took the form of children's fairy tales, and may have contained a cathartic working out of her own childhood experience with her father.

At this period Christina had to stifle her negative feelings about her brother William and Lucy, who were agnostic and did not baptise their children. Her relationship with Lucy was problematic. Eventually Christina and her mother moved to 30 Torrington Square together with her two aunts, Charlotte and Eliza, where they managed on their own resources. However, they were not to live there long before Maria was struck down by cancer, which must have progressed very fast: the symptoms arose in July 1876 and she died in November, in spite of surgical interventions. It is hardly surprising that grief is a persistent theme of Christina's writing around this period. She underwent further stress with her brother Dante Gabriel's dependency on chloral (a sleep-promoting drug), which rose to a serious level, involving severe depression. He was persuaded to move to a farmhouse in the Herne Bay area: Christina, her mother, and a nurse joined him and helped him to recover to a limited extent, though he remained a source of anxiety.

Christina always managed somehow to continue writing: her creative fire was not foiled. At the time of Maria's illness she completed a new book with the title *Young Plants and Polished Corners*, a devotional volume based on the red-letter saints' days (special feast days in the Church calendar, originally printed in red), linked to appropriate seasonal wild flowers—a genuinely original idea. For twelve of the feasts she wrote new poems. Further poems followed, in particular the *Ballad of Boding*, which has an adventurous free rhythm and gripping imagery. She also completed more devotional works, in particular *Benedicite, Omnia Opera*.

In 1880 a new work, *Manna Innominata*, a collection of 14 sonnets from an un-named woman, possibly included an element of Christina's buried love for Cayley, but also much more of a universal nature. Mainly however it addresses the painful question: 'Youth gone, and beauty gone, what doth remain?' But physically Christina was now much better. Hardly surprisingly she objected to the mid-Victorian trend towards pornography, and viewed with disfavour Charles Dodgson's nude photographs of young girls. This must have revived her traumatic memories of her own adolescence.

In January 1881 James Collinson, her fiancé of 30 years earlier, died, and Christina published a new sonnet sequence with the title *Later Life*.

> *We lack, yet cannot fix upon the lack:*
> *Not this, not that; yet somewhat, certainly*
> *We see the things we do not yearn to see*
> *Around us; and what see we glancing back?*
> *Lost hopes that leave our hearts upon the rack,*
> *Hopes that were never ours yet seemed to be,*
> *For which we steered on life's salt stormy sea...* [11]

Christina continued to publish with Macmillan, with a third collected volume entitled *A Pageant and Other Poems*, which added to her already outstanding reputation. But family problems summoned her again: she and her mother were called to Dante Gabriel's bedside after he had a stroke, and cared for him until he died in 1883. Dante Gabriel's problems had always been mental as well as physical, and he died an unbeliever, to Christina's distress.

Again, Christina was drawn to somewhat radical views, in response to the British 'victory' in Kandahar in 1880, [12] which resulted in many deaths, and the bombardment of Alexandria in response to insurrection in Egypt in 1887. She recoiled from the murder of Afghans, and also of Egyptians. This moral stance was reflected in her new book *Letter and Spirit*. It was generous in spirit and not censorious, and she seems to have come near to forgiving her own father as she widened her discourse to include God the Father as well as God the Son.

A further campaign to which Christina lent her support was that to raise the age of consent from 12 to 14: in fact it was only raised to 13 in 1875, and did not stop the traffic in teenage girls from Britain to Belgium for sale to brothels, or the exploitation of young girls in London. The link between this campaign and Christina's own probable teenage experience is clear.

Time Flies was her next publication, a diary with poems and prose for every day of the year, and the nearest she came to an autobiography. Saints' days are a special feature. Time was indeed flying, and Christina's mother, for whom Christina had faithfully cared over many years, finally declined and died in April 1886. Christina must have been worn out, and some of her old headaches returned, as well as depression. She was also still caring for her two aunts, aged 87 and 80.

Her duties of housekeeping and nursing occupied a good deal of her time, but she also continued to write, her new book being entitled *The Face of the Deep*. This was a commentary on the last book of the Bible, the *Revelation of St John the Divine*, with poems and philosophical reflection, including again the theme of animal rights, and even that of ethnic equality and diversity, welcoming people of every nation: 'whites with blacks, all ranks with all ranks, all men with all men.' She also lashed out at the luxuries of the rich, surrounded by the poor and needy. The book was finally published in 1892.

In 1893 she published a collection of devotional poetry with the title *Verses*. With the death of Tennyson in 1892 the most obvious candidate for the position of Poet Laureate was certainly Christina, but the accolade was not to be hers. Alfred Austin, an undistinguished and somewhat jingoistic poet, was finally appointed in 1896.

In the same year (1892) Christina discovered her breast cancer. She felt a double lump in her left breast, and a Dr Stewart was summoned. A mastectomy was performed, and she resumed her nursing duties to her remaining aunt Eliza, who finally died in 1893. However, Christina's cancer recurred, and her condition deteriorated swiftly, so that by August 1894 she was confined to bed; and in great pain, it seems, both physical and spiritual, not helped by her confessor, who seems to have added to Christina's torture rather than relieving it. She died on 29th December, praying to the very end.

For many people Christina Rossetti is known only as the poet who wrote a favourite Christmas carol, 'In the bleak mid-winter', set to music by Gustav Holst. But her work is far-ranging in its breadth and depth, and is only in our 21st century being recognized for its true value. She was 63 when breast cancer finally caught up with her, at a time when she was looking after her aunt and could pay little attention to her own health, or indeed to poetry either. It is hardly surprising that the disease progressed swiftly.

But looking back on her life, it is perhaps not fanciful to suggest that her poetry saved her many times from gloom that might have overwhelmed her, and perhaps also staved off physical illness by offering a productive outlet for her emotions. Her creative fire went not into child-bearing but into poetry, to our great advantage. It was not finally extinguished until she reached the mature age (for those times) of 65.

Select Bibliography

Jan Marsh: *Christina Rossetti: A Literary Biography* (Jonathan Cape, London, 1994; Pimlico edition, Random House, London, 1995)

Christina Rossetti: *The Complete Poems*, ed. R. W. Crump, notes and introduction by Betty S. Flowers (Penguin Books, London, 2001)

David Wright (ed.):   *Seven Victorian Poets* (Heinemann Educational Books, London, 1964)

Notes

1. Marsh, p. 48.
2. *The Complete Poems*, p. 664.
3. Marsh, p. 62.
4. *ibid.*, p. 77.
5. From 'Song': *The Complete Poems*, p. 52.
6. *ibid.*, p. 763.
7. *ibid.*, p. 796.
8. Marsh, p. 216.
9. *The Complete Poems*, p. 17.
10. *ibid.*, pp. 742–3.
11. *ibid.*, p. 348.
12. The Battle of Kandahar, 1st September 1880, was the last major struggle of the Second Anglo-Afghan War. The battle in southern Afghanistan was fought between the British army under General Roberts and the Afghan forces led by Ayub Khan. It ended with a decisive British victory, having inflicted nearly 3,000 casualties.

Princess Victoria, the Empress Friedrich III

THE ELDEST CHILD OF QUEEN VICTORIA and Prince Albert was born on 21st November 1840. She was the princess Victoria Adelaide Mary Louisa, usually known as Vicky, and until her brother Bertie, later King Edward VII, was born the next year, she was the heir presumptive to the English crown. She was breast-fed by a wet-nurse, was looked after as a small child by the admirable Lady Lyttelton, and then had her education supervised by Baron Stockmar of Coburg. She had both French and German tutors before the age of four and was exceptionally bright, far outshining her younger brothers and sisters. At the age of six serious study began, with reading, writing, arithmetic, dictation, poetry, history, Scripture, German, French, music, dancing, drawing and painting.

The royal family lived partly at Buckingham Palace and partly at Windsor Castle, and they went on holiday to Osborne House on the Isle of Wight. In 1851, when Prince Wilhelm of Prussia and his wife Augusta were invited to the opening of the Great Exhibition in London, Vicky, now aged 10, met Fritz, their eldest son, who at 19 was still a student but already an army officer. Vicky's German was considerably more fluent than Fritz's English, and she enchanted him. In 1855 he visited England again. By then Vicky was nearly 15, good-looking, with beautiful blue eyes, clever but naïve, and, like many well-brought-up Victorian teenagers, ignorant of the 'facts of life'.

Fritz was entertained at Balmoral, and went hunting with Prince Albert. He was immediately attracted to Vicky, and she to him. 'She possesses great feeling and intelligence and has a lively interest in art and literature',[1] Fritz reported to his parents. In fact in the same year, during which charitable funds were being raised in aid of sufferers in the Crimean war:

> ...an exhibition of amateur paintings in aid of the Patriotic Fund was staged at Burlington House in Bond Street by one of the queen's favourite art dealers, Ernest Gambart. It included donations of drawings and watercolours by the five eldest royal

children. One work in particular by Victoria, the Princess Royal, caused quite a stir. A semicircular painting, subsequently known as The Field of Battle, depicted a dying Grenadier on the field of Inkerman in the arms of his beautiful wife… it was by far the best work in the exhibition. [2]

In Balmoral, Fritz approached the Queen and Prince Albert with a proposal of marriage to Vicky, and was joyfully accepted, with the proviso that Fritz must not propose to Vicky herself until she was 16, and the actual marriage had to wait until she was 17. However, promises were overtaken by events: soon afterwards the couple managed to fall behind their companions on a walk, and exchanged their first kiss. Vicky told her parents that she loved the prince. The young couple kissed again in the presence of Victoria and Albert, and the alliance was sealed. Vicky had only just experienced her first menstruation.

The royal engagement lasted almost two years, during which the couple were not supposed to be left alone, though when young brother Bertie was the chaperone, this sometimes slipped. But more importantly, Vicky had to be prepared for a difficult diplomatic role, as a link between Prussia, allied with Russia, and Britain, which had fought Russia in the Crimean war. Her father hoped that the German states would unite under Prussia and look towards Britain rather than Russia. He gave Vicky daily lessons in history and statecraft, while Victoria prepared her elaborate trousseau. Vicky and Fritz wrote long letters to each other, and in January 1858 they were married in the Chapel Royal, St James's, with Mendelssohn's wedding march being played for the first time at a royal wedding. In February the couple set off for Prussia. Vicky had been well prepared by her father for her diplomatic role, and she and her husband were in love: what could possibly go wrong?

They crossed the Channel in the snow, and arrived at Antwerp the next morning. Uncle Leopold met them and escorted them to Brussels, where a ball was held in their honour. The next day they set off again by train for Berlin, stopping at stations on the way to greet crowds of well-wishers. Finally they entered Berlin through the Brandenburg Gate in a gilded coach. Crowds of Berliners greeted them, and they arrived at their destination, the Old Castle (Schloss Charlottenburg), where they were greeted by King Friedrich Wilhelm IV (Fritz's uncle), and Queen Elisabeth. Vicky and Fritz received a warm welcome (in spite of the Queen's Anglophobia) and Vicky was admired. Fritz claimed in a telegram that 'the whole Royal Family is enchanted with my wife'.[3]

But Vicky was taking on a huge task, to become a successful Prussian wife. She had now joined the Hohenzollern family, which though Protestant was hostile to the kind of constitutional parliamentary government that she was familiar with. The Prussians were primarily successful as soldiers, and the family was authoritarian, militaristic, and conservative, in contrast to the more liberal values taught to her by her father. When Vicky arrived in Berlin at the age of 17, she was confronted with many problems of statecraft that, in spite of her father's careful preparation, must have been extremely daunting. For a start, her parents-in-law were on uneasy terms with each other, and she had to tread carefully (instructed by her mother's letters) with her new relations. Queen Victoria wrote to her daughter several times a week, and Prince Albert once a week. In return Victoria demanded a detailed account of all Vicky's activities. Vicky had a wonderful relationship with Fritz, going on long drives with him, but was also obliged to attend court functions such as dinners, plays and operas, and was still studying hard.

She and Fritz lived in considerable discomfort in the Old Castle, until a bathroom was built there with hot and cold running water. The place was icy and draughty, and Vicky caught a nasty cold during her first few days there. Each spring the Prussian court moved to its summer palace, Babelsberg, in Potsdam, and Vicky and Fritz went with them. The palace was picturesque but fairly uncomfortable. However, the young couple were in love, and Vicky was soon pregnant. Victorian custom decreed that intercourse should not take place during pregnancy, and Vicky suffered many of the usual problems, such as morning sickness and dizziness.

She and Fritz moved into their own palace in Berlin, next to the Opera House. Vicky's mother was bombarding her with constant letters of advice and instructions on how to behave, sometimes at odds with local customs, to Vicky's great distress. But worse was to follow: her first child was a breech birth, and both child and mother nearly died. The little boy was born with a defective arm and probably slight brain damage. He was named Friedrich Wilhelm Victor Albert, and eventually became Kaiser Wilhelm II of Germany.

Vicky followed royal custom and engaged a wet-nurse to feed her baby. His doctors tried various devices to improve his defective arm, with varying success, and he grew up enjoying a great deal of maternal attention as a result. But when he was only four months old, Vicky paid a 12-day visit to her parents, leaving him behind. On this visit she and her mother were more like sisters, sharing their experiences of motherhood. On her return, Fritz took command of an Infantry Division.

Vicky gave birth to a girl in July 1860. Though the birth was easier than her first confinement, the remarks from the Russian relatives at her choice of names (Victoria Elizabeth Augusta Charlotte, known as Charlotte) upset Vicky. This squabble about names only illustrated the more significant conflict between the Russian and British interest in Prussian politics, with Vicky in the middle of it all, trying to keep the peace. Her mother also gave her the job of finding suitable royal spouses for her siblings, notably Bertie (16) and Alice (15). This involved much heartache.

The Prussian King Friedrich Wilhelm IV died on New Year's Day 1861 and was succeeded by his brother, Wilhelm I, Fritz's father. Thus Fritz and Vicky became the Crown Prince and Princess Friedrich and Victoria von Hohenzollern. The new King, aged 64, was flattered by the Order of the Garter bestowed on him by Queen Victoria but was paranoid about plots, relying on spies to alert him to talk of insurrection, and was even suspicious of his own family. Vicky wrote home that 'It is neither an easy nor a pleasant life.'[4] Then at the end of the year her own father, Prince Albert, died. She had adored him and had seen him as her political adviser and intellectual mainstay in circumstances in which she was uncomfortable with the illiberal atmosphere of the Prussian court. 'Where shall I look to for advice? I am only 21 and things here wear a threatening aspect',[5] she wrote to her mother.

Even more poignantly, she had written in 1858, 'There are such thousands of things I would like to hear Papa's opinion about. Whatever I hear or see I always think what would Papa say what would he think. Dear Papa always has been my oracle.'[6] The problem was that the Prussian military establishment was taking precedence over the two houses of parliament in political decision-making. Fritz, with liberal tendencies, found himself in opposition to his father, who was militaristic and conservative, and also frightened of a repetition of the 1848 revolution. In the end Bismarck (Count Otto Eduard Leopold von Bismarck-Schönhausen) was appointed as Prime Minister, and supported Wilhelm's monarchical and anti-democratic stance, much to the regret of Fritz and Vicky.

'Our affairs here are in a lamentable state—indecisions, confusions and mistakes of all kinds and sorts are *l'ordre du jour*', wrote Vicky to her mother.[7] Bismarck looked to Russia for support in his anti-democratic policy. Vicky and Fritz escaped to celebrate the marriage of Vicky's brother Bertie to Alix of Denmark, but Bismarck disapproved and Vicky wrote: 'I never thought it would be as bad and as hopeless as all this'.[8] Under Bismarck, free speech was not allowed. Vicky and Fritz were unable to challenge Bismarck openly and yet miserably unhappy with his press censorship. Fritz's father, Wilhelm I, was under the thumb of Bismarck.

Bismarck then managed to frustrate a meeting between Wilhelm I and the other German powers, fearing an alliance between Prussia and Austria, and continued to undermine the constitution, causing Fritz, caught between filial loyalty and political conscience, much distress. He exploited the differences between father and son, with Vicky valiantly trying to keep up Fritz's morale. Even Vicky's relationship with her own mother was regarded by Bismarck as a political problem, since he saw Britain as rivalling Russia, with which Prussia was allied. But in spite of all his efforts to undermine constitutional government, the Prussian Chamber of Deputies (the lower house of parliament) returned a liberal majority in 1863. Vicky spent a brief holiday in Balmoral with her mother and her three children, and retained her fighting spirit in spite of losing the support and advice of her beloved father, Prince Albert.

Then King Leopold I of Belgium, Victoria's uncle, died, leaving Vicky without her three valued political mentors: her father, Baron Stockmar, and now Uncle Leopold. After all these losses, her little son Sigismund died of meningitis. She was also worried about her son Willy, about whom she had earlier written to her mother:

> *The poor arm is no better, and Willy begins to feel being behind much smaller boys in every exercise of the body. He cannot run fast because he has no balance, nor ride nor climb, nor cut his food etc. I wonder he is as good tempered about it. His tutor thinks he will feel it much more, and be much unhappier about it as he grows older and feels himself debarred from everything which others enjoy—and particularly so as he is so strong and lively and healthy! It is a hard trial for him and for us.[9]*

Vicky was often out of sympathy with Prussian policy as she lived through the events leading up to the unification of a large part of German-speaking Europe under the leadership of Prussia: the annexation of Schleswig and Holstein from Denmark by Prussia and Austria in 1864, the Austro-Prussian War of 1866 and the Franco-Prussian War of 1870, at the outbreak of which she was still not quite 30 and had just given birth to her seventh child, Sophie.

In 1869 she had attended a meeting of the International Congress in Aid of the Wounded and later wrote to her mother that 'we have the horrible prospect of the most terrible war Europe has yet known'.[8] But when the war with France came in 1870 and her husband was a Prussian general, she was delighted with his success at the Battle of Sedan and with his subsequent promotion to the rank of Field Marshal, and she wrote moralizing messages to her mother about the frivolity of the French. She busied herself with working for the war-wounded and was able to use supplies of old linen sent to her by her mother.

The successful Prussian armies and the armies of the allied German states reached Versailles, and in the Hall of Mirrors of Louis XIV's palace King Wilhelm of Prussia was proclaimed German Emperor, or Kaiser. In the elaborate German victory parade through Paris the 12-year-old Wilhelm rode successfully in spite of his disabled left arm, and later that year Fritz and Vicky visited Queen Victoria in Osborne on the Isle of Wight. Soon Vicky was pregnant again and another girl ('Mossy') was born in April 1872. The French Emperor Napoleon III and his wife, Empress Eugénie, were now in exile in England, while in France, after some years of uncertainty, the Third Republic was established in 1875.

Bismarck, who is one of the outstanding figures of 19th-century history, had managed to unify a large part of the German-speaking territories of Europe. By ensuring that the areas controlled by the Habsburgs were excluded from the new German Empire he ensured that Prussia would be the dominant element in that empire. He had been successful as Minister President of Prussia. Now he was similarly successful as Chancellor of the new German Empire, controlling both internal and foreign policy, initiating legislation in the imperial parliament, appointing all other ministers, and answerable only to the Kaiser.

A common currency, uniform weights and measures, a central bank, a unified railway system, a unified postal and telegraph service, a common code of law, one national army and one administrative service, together with measures to protect German industry from foreign competition, helped the development of a powerful nation with a rapidly growing economy. To someone brought up in the very different political climate of England it could seem excessively autocratic, but to many Germans their constitution, with an effective executive ruling within the laws established by an imperial parliament, seemed to compare favourably with, on the one hand, the despotisms of Russia and the Ottoman Empire in the East and, on the other hand, what they saw as the mob rule of the French Republic and of British parliamentary democracy in the West.

In the meantime Fritz and Vicky struggled to keep a spirit of liberalism alive. Fritz supported the emancipation of women and various other worthy causes. Not for Vicky were only *Kinder, Küche, Kirche* (a German slogan meaning 'children, kitchen, church', the proper concerns of women). She had a brain that she used in many ways: her home was renowned for its liberal outlook and patronage of the arts. She continued with a variety of studies as well as with music and painting.

Vicky was very concerned to care for her children herself, and she breast-fed her last five babies, though it went against royal tradition. That might have helped to ward off breast cancer. The family enjoyed country pursuits: they bought a farm and used it for summer holidays, even starting a new village school. But Fritz was away a lot on army duties, so the children's education fell largely to Vicky. Even though she was not extravagant and took on many duties herself, with eight children born in 15 years, she still had a considerable staff of maids, governesses and so on. But she loved her children and spent much time with them.

Her mother-in-law was by no means attentive to either her daughter-in-law or her grandchildren, even forgetting their birthdays, whereas Queen Victoria was constantly showering presents on her grandchildren, who paid frequent visits to England. One disappointment was her eldest grandson, Willy, who became increasingly arrogant. Vicky engaged a tutor for Willy, a Calvinist, Georg Hintzpeter, who enforced a very strict régime. Apparently drawing and music were banned, as unsuitable for kings. Renunciation, discipline, and duty were the watchwords. Hintzpeter was stern and insistent on riding lessons until Willy overcame the physical disabilities that had crippled him since birth. Hintzpeter also took Willy on factory visits, so he learned about the conditions of the workers. But most important of all was the army: Willy's first military parade was when he was only 10. Vicky was not at all happy about this. She was more comfortable with his interest in the navy.

Vicky's daughter Charlotte was born soon after Willy, and though pretty had some difficult characteristics. Then came Henry, an awkward child. Five more children followed, of whom four survived. Vicky had to manage all her children during her husband's long absences at the front. Like Victoria herself, Vicky did not care for the endless balls and parties that were *de rigueur* at court, nor did she like late nights. But she took Willy with her to an international exhibition in

Vienna. She wrote to her mother: 'the Exhibition interests me immensely but I am so sick of ceremonies, etiquette, dress, show, fatigue and waste of time.'[10] However, a great attraction, particularly for Willy, was the Empress Elisabeth of Austria: according to Vicky her 'beauty seems more marvellous to me each time I see her'.[11]

In the following year, Vicky spent much time attempting to counteract the machinations of Bismarck. She tried to get Germany, Austria, Italy, and France to co-operate in order to achieve a settlement between the Turks and the Russians. Vicky was not usually fooled by Bismarck, but on this occasion she was, and Russia declared war on the Turks, much to the distress of both Vicky and her mother, who together with Disraeli supported Turkey. Vicky's main concern was to stop the bloodshed. Finally Russia ceased hostilities. A congress was held in Berlin in 1878: Disraeli dined with Bismarck, and characterized him as a complete despot. Disraeli did well for England at the Congress, which lasted a month. But issues in the Balkans were left unresolved, and the consequent conflicts beset Europe until the First World War.

In 1878, just before the Congress in Berlin, there was an attempt on Wilhelm I's life, which didn't wound him severely, and then another, which did. Vicky and Fritz were visiting Queen Victoria, but rushed back home. In spite of his incapacity he insisted on continuing to rule instead of handing over to his son. Bismarck took the opportunity to impose martial law on Berlin and consolidate his power. Vicky however was not unduly perturbed, and among all the talk of socialism bought a copy of Karl Marx's *Das Kapital*.

In 1878 she also told her mother that the Social Democratic Party had done well in the elections to the Reichstag, though Bismarck quickly passed a bill enabling fines and imprisonment of dissenters, including publishers. Many socialists were arrested. It was only Fritz's efforts that saved the Reichstag from an even more stringent law. Vicky wrote to Queen Victoria: 'Many many tender thanks for all your kindness the recollection of which will cheer me — when back at Berlin in a milieu which wants no common strength of mind not to be utterly depressed and become bitter. I fancy I have braved it for 21 years with patience and I hope with courage: but there is nothing to render life attractive there.'[12]

Even worse, the 'dearest and nicest and most promising'[13] of her sons, Waldemar, died of diphtheria. This was a shattering blow. To add insult, Bismarck gave an 'enormous soirée with all the parliamentary people'[14] on the evening of Waldemar's funeral. Soon after Waldemar's death Vicky became a grandmother, at the age of only 38, to Charlotte's baby daughter. As well as grieving for Waldemar, she had hormonal problems. Her in-laws were unsympathetic, and Vicky suffered severe depression. She went to Italy and slowly improved during the winter, but no one could fill the gap left by Waldemar.

Vicky felt unattractive, her hair growing grey and her face wrinkled. But her warm relationship with her husband endured—unlike many royal marriages. She spent eight months recuperating in Italy, but news of political machinations reached her, and she was particularly concerned to keep Constantinople (now Istanbul) out of the hands of Russia. But when Czar Alexander II was assassinated in March 1881 the scenario changed again. The League of the Three Emperors (*Dreikaiserbund*—between Germany, Austria-Hungary and Russia) was signed, and liberal values took a tumble. The League remained a secret treaty until 1919. The cause of liberalism was quashed. England had been rejected by Germany in favour of Russia. Now it was Fritz who became depressed.

At this point we might pause and consider Vicky's emotional history. She had a happy childhood, as far as we know, and a very close relationship with both parents. Her father was a role model and a true friend, and she was devastated when he died. Her relationship with her husband was loving and loyal, but both of them experienced many frustrations and political difficulties, besides grief with the death of two sons. Both suffered from depression. In both cases their creative fire, which was immense, encountered setbacks and problems.

In spite of Bismarck's best efforts, socialism flourished. In the Reichstag, with two-thirds of the seats won by those opposed to him, he then campaigned against the Crown Prince and Princess, worried that they would promote liberalism and a pro-British policy. Bismarck's spy ingratiated himself with Vicky and repeated inside information to his master. Sadly, Vicky's two sons Willy and Henry were impressed by Bismarck, whose aim was to unify Germany and dominate western Europe, with the enemies being the Poles, who as Catholics were suspects, and the Jews: anti-Semitism was nothing new. Vicky was very upset by this intolerance, even writing to her mother about an anti-Semitic pamphlet by Richard Wagner: 'I never read anything so violent, conceited or unfair.'[15] Violence followed. Vicky became chair of an orphanage for Jewish girls founded in Berlin. Both Fritz and Vicky were horrified by the anti-Semitic movement, and did all they could to oppose it. So began the campaign that ended 60 years later in the Holocaust.

While up till now Vicky had done her best to be a good German, now she was worn out by Bismarck's machinations and turned increasingly to England, as her letters to her mother illustrate. There followed a colonial competition with England—the purpose of which was to drive a wedge between England and the Crown Prince, just as much as to gain territory. Vicky had great faith in Britain as a benign influence on foreign peoples, but Bismarck did his utmost to undermine relations with Britain.

Germany's colonial adventures never amounted to much. Bismarck had to turn his attention to Europe, where the Balkan states were being oppressed by Turkey. Vicky's distress at his manoeuvres was compounded by the behaviour of her own son Willy, who was sent to St Petersburg by Bismarck instead of his father, Fritz, to cement the League of the Three Emperors (Russia, Germany and Austria-

Hungary). This also involved thwarting the desire of Vicky's daughter Moretta (Viktoria) to marry Sandro of Battenberg, Prince of Bulgaria, to whom she was very attached. Even Queen Victoria was enlisted to comfort and advise. The affair further widened the breach between Vicky and her son Willy.

The problem was that the Battenbergs were not considered to be of true royal blood, and so not suitable for marriage to Hohenzollerns. Further scandals followed: Vicky's niece Princess Victoria of Hesse married Sandro's older brother Prince Louis of Battenberg, and Queen Victoria's youngest daughter Beatrice became engaged to Sandro's younger brother Prince Henry of Battenberg. This provoked shock and horror among members of the Hohenzollern royal family, except for Vicky, who supported the Battenbergs. They were married in 1885.

Politically things went from bad to worse as far as Vicky was concerned. Bismarck was determined to thwart any liberal tendencies, which she and Fritz supported. With the decline in health of Wilhelm I, Vicky tried to effect a rapprochement with Bismarck in preparation for her husband Fritz to take over as emperor. But Bismarck remained antagonistic, asserting that Vicky continued to be an Englishwoman with no feeling for Germany.

In the following year Fritz's voice gave rise to concern, and finally cancer of the larynx was suspected and Morell Mackenzie, an eminent Scottish specialist with a practice in Harley Street, London, was summoned. He removed part of the tumour for a pathological report. Fritz was worried that events would overtake him, that his father would die and his son Willy take over if his own health deteriorated further. But both father and son appeared with Vicky on the great occasion of Queen Victoria's Jubilee in June 1887. Fritz attended the main event, the service in Westminster Abbey, but otherwise was engaged in visits to Harley Street to see his surgeon, Mackenzie.

Meanwhile Bismarck was up to his usual tricks, spreading the rumour of an affair between Vicky and her Court Chamberlain, Count Seckendorff. Sadly this story was widely believed, further undermining Vicky's position. But Vicky and Fritz went to Italy, to give Fritz a chance to recuperate, though Fritz had to ask Mackenzie for further consultations, and a new tumour was discovered. With both the Emperor and his son threatened with imminent demise, grandson Willy (now 28) was emboldened to interfere. He wanted a laryngectomy carried out. Fritz thought this would be too risky, and there ensued a battle between those who wanted him to have an operation and those who did not. It was even suggested that the problem was caused by syphilis, not cancer — another rumour instigated by Bismarck. Moreover, Willy was appointed without Fritz's knowledge to sign official papers, since the Emperor himself was now failing. This was a humiliating setback for Fritz.

Journalists gathered round, greedy for news. Vicky's old friend Lady Ponsonby, on a visit, noted that Vicky kept up a brave face for Fritz but broke down in tears when alone with her. Relations started visiting, causing more problems. Meanwhile Willy was preparing for the demise of his father and grandfather, only too anxious to ascend the throne. Even Bismarck disapproved of his inappropriate haste. In early 1888 Fritz underwent a tracheotomy, which left him unable to speak. Mackenzie disagreed with the German doctors about the course of further treatment, which led to more difficulties for Fritz and Vicky. But the next dramatic event was the death of Fritz's father, before Fritz could visit him. He inherited the imperial title and became Kaiser Friedrich III, King of Prussia. He immediately honoured Vicky with the Order of the Black Eagle.

Since Fritz was now unable to speak, he communicated in writing, and much of this survives. He wrote to his surgeon, Mackenzie, 'I thank you for having made me live long enough to recompense the valiant courage of my wife.'[16] He presented Bismarck with a liberal manifesto that included religious tolerance. However, there were those in Berlin who eagerly anticipated Fritz's death, especially Bismarck's son Herbert.

The funeral of Wilhelm I was a very grand and solemn affair, the procession led by Willy in the absence of his father, who watched from a window. Fritz proceeded to distribute further honours to those who had given significant service to his father, including Jews and others not approved by conservatives. The next duty was to sign hundreds of state papers, including two left over from the previous reign, which Fritz only signed under pressure. Again, a deputy had to be found, and Vicky was passed over in favour of her son Willy, who gloried in his new-found status.

Then came a deterioration in Fritz's health, with a clash between his English and German doctors about his treatment. Queen Victoria paid him a visit, warned by her Prime Minister, Lord Salisbury, to be wary of Willy's self-important posturing. The Queen also had a meeting with Bismarck to discuss affairs of state, which seems to have gone well: 'That was a woman; one could do business with her', he commented afterwards.[17] She was accompanied by her Indian secretary, the Munshi Abdul Karim. Vicky, like her mother, seemed unusually (for the time) free of racism, which was not the case with the royal family back home. Later she was to visit Karim's wife in her cottage. Now she was in a state of acute distress, having to watch the suffering of her husband and also under political attack by so many forces antagonistic to the English influence. However, Victoria's visit cheered her up to some extent. It had been a great success with everyone except her grandson Willy, who thought it was high time the Queen died.

In June 1888 Fritz and Vicky moved to the Neues Palais, renamed Friedrichskron, in Potsdam. The Kaiser showed great fortitude in bearing his illness, and was always courteous to visitors and guests. But he had not long to live: finally his cancer caught up with him, and he died on 15th June 1888, surrounded by his children. His son Willy made sure that the mourning and interment followed swiftly and was definitely low-key, with no international guests. Even so, the Prince and Princess of

Wales managed to attend the funeral, and Fritz's short life was honoured by many who respected his liberalism, including Gladstone, the British Prime Minister. But his eldest son, now Wilhelm II, did his best to forget his father as speedily as possible, and Bismarck did not even bother to call on his mother with condolences. Wilhelm hurried off to St Petersburg to meet his friend Alexander III, disregarding his grandmother Queen Victoria and the etiquette of mourning.

Willy was also very stingy to his mother, denying her an appropriate palace in which to live. Further humiliations followed. Vicky wanted to honour Fritz's memory, and the part he had played in the Franco-Prussian war and the unification of Germany, whereas others attributed the founding of the German Empire to Bismarck. Excerpts from Fritz's diary that illustrated the point were published in a German magazine by an old friend of Fritz's, Professor Gefferken, who was imprisoned for three months by Bismarck for his pains. The reason that Bismarck was so incensed by the publication of Fritz's diaries was that he wanted to take sole credit for the formation of the German Empire.

Vicky grew more and more miserable, bereft of the love of her life and denigrated by her son. She even felt suicidal: 'Yesterday I felt very near putting an end to myself.'[18] She found solace in charitable work. The next major crisis in Germany was the miners' strike of 1889, over which Bismarck and Wilhelm II disagreed. The Kaiser was actually on the side of the workers, while Bismarck was with the owners. For once Willy was sympathetic to liberal causes, like his mother. After many more comings and goings, Bismarck finally resigned as Chancellor, and retired to the country. But Bismarck's departure did not help the relationship between Willy and his mother. When Augusta, Willy's grandmother, died, Willy made sure that her various honorary titles pertaining to charitable work, including the chairmanship of the Red Cross, passed not to Vicky but to his wife Dona, even though Vicky was the person who had worked tirelessly for the sick and wounded. This upset Vicky greatly.

However, Vicky continued with her charitable work, attending various functions of philanthropic organizations, founding a children's hospital, and in staffing hospital wards taking an ecumenical view, by engaging Catholics and Jews as well as Protestants. Like her mother's, Vicky's mourning was profound, and Willy's avoidance of her made things even worse. To add insult to injury he refused permission to build an equestrian statue of his father, even though the Berliners had already raised the money. Further frustrations followed, mainly owing to Willy. But at least on her 50th birthday there was lunch at the Kaiser's palace, and with Bismarck out of the way, life became more bearable.

At the same time Willy was withdrawing from his Russian alliance and seeking rapprochement with Britain, greatly enjoying his annual visits to Cowes for Regatta Week. Vicky now came into her own as Willy's messenger to Paris, where she went on a mission to contact French artists to take part in a forthcoming international exhibition in Berlin. Sadly the visit turned out badly, as a rightist faction twisted it to their advantage, claiming that the Dowager Empress had offended the French by visiting significant sites such as Saint-Cloud, which had been destroyed by the Germans in the Franco-Prussian war. Subsequently some of the chosen painters refused to exhibit in Berlin. Now Willy was on bad terms with both his old enemy France and also his former friend Russia, while these two countries drew closer together, forming a threat to Germany.

Although his new Chancellor, Caprivi, tried to restrain his more erratic moves, Wilhelm II's arbitrary and capricious behaviour both at home and abroad caused Vicky consternation. He was ferociously anti-Semitic. He was also fond of extravagance and show, and kept extremely busy performing official activities, such as launching ships and opening buildings. His court was lavishly furnished and extremely formal. But above all came the army, on which Willy wished to spend far too much, ignoring other budgetary needs such as education. As for Vicky, her widowhood was poignantly sad; she also suffered frustration and despair with her son's rule.

Vicky was still writing to her mother at least three times a week. As for her own increasing family, her children were marrying and producing grandchildren, making her happy even though visits to her were limited, especially by her daughter-in-law Dona. The crowning irony was when Bismarck actually appealed to Vicky to help patch things up between him and her son Willy — when Bismarck had been the cause of the rift between her and her son. She and Willy did however achieve superficial reconciliation at a meeting in Berlin.

Vicky continued to be hurt by Willy's neglect of her, and by his wife's desire to keep her grandchildren away as well. But things improved when in 1894 she moved into a new home, Schloss Friedrichshof. This was her own house, bought with her own money, and she now felt safe. It had been carefully designed in a neo-Gothic style and had many modern conveniences. She was very house-proud, and paid her servants well. She also continued to be generous to charitable good causes.

Riding had long been one of her pastimes, and now she rode every day — apparently with great skill. She also read widely in her library. She cared for her estate, planting trees and restoring buildings. She even worked at her painting. Her new castle gave her the opportunity for much entertainment, particularly of her large and increasing family, including grandchildren. Even Willy started visiting more often, though inconveniently accompanied by a large entourage. But his mental ill-health increased, with intermittent rages and breakdowns, and Vicky was chronically anxious about him.

Willy's annual visit to Cowes was a great occasion for showing off, and he overdid it in 1895, by taking along four warships to what should have been a purely social occasion. They got in the way of the racing and were an embarrassment. A rendezvous with the Prime Minister, Lord Salisbury, did not go according to plan. Tensions between England and Germany continued, in spite of Vicky's best efforts.

After a long illness involving gangrene of the foot, Bismarck finally died, and the necessary ceremonies were performed. Vicky herself now had to face serious illness. She was out riding when her horse shied at a thresher and threw her. Luckily she was not seriously hurt and was able to get up and walk away, but the doctor who examined her later observed a large tumour in her breast.

Vicky reacted with typical stoicism, not wishing to tell people or receive sympathy. She told her Lord Chamberlain, Baron Reichshach: 'There is no reason for alarm. I have trained myself the whole of my life to be able to resist illness… my body is as hard as steel…'[19] The diagnosis was confirmed by another German doctor, who observed that the cancer had already metastasized and was inoperable. Her pain increased, especially in her back. She had a brief remission in April 1900, and an English doctor, Francis Laking, prescribed morphine, which helped.

Vicky now got around in a wheelchair. In May 1900 she celebrated Queen Victoria's birthday with a grand family gathering, photos and all. But the disease progressed and she was in a great deal of pain. She thought she was not as brave as her husband, but this seems unlikely: she appears to have been extremely stoical. Her brother the Duke of Coburg also suffered from cancer, this time of the larynx, like Fritz, but apparently without knowing the diagnosis. She herself however wanted to know everything, though it seems all the same that doctors were economical with the truth, calling spinal metastases by euphemisms such as 'lumbago' or 'neuralgia'. They also reassured her that the pain would go — which of course it didn't.

This avoidance of speaking about cancer will have been familiar to many patients in more recent times, who were patronized with talk of 'naughty cells' and similar euphemisms not so long ago. Vicky suffered terribly, with acute pain, and the German doctors did not allow her much morphine. In November 1900 she 'celebrated' her 60th birthday. Her arms and hands were swollen, and her wedding ring had to be sawn off.

The next family event was the death of Queen Victoria, which seems to have been peaceful. She was surrounded by all her children and grandchildren, even Willy, except of course for Vicky, who was too ill to travel. Her brother Bertie (now King Edward VII) visited Germany in 1901 with Dr Laking in tow: he was officially attending on Bertie rather than Vicky, to avoid upsetting the Germans, but he once again prescribed morphine for her. Vicky enjoyed a brief pain-free interlude while she interrogated Bertie on many important matters. She then entrusted her precious letters to Bertie for safe conduct back home.

Even at this stage of her life, when she was suffering acute and constant pain, she managed to find time and energy for encouraging her daughter Sophie to support charity work in Greece, and even attempted to learn Greek herself. She also made a will, remembering everyone who had helped her in her lifetime. In the end her son Willy remained at her bedside during her last hours and was there when she died. Her daughters Sophie and Mossy arrived shortly afterwards. Vicky had left instructions for a simple funeral with no speeches. But Willy managed to insult his mother even in death by spreading a story that she wished to be buried naked, draped in the Union Jack, and sent to England for burial. Sir Henry Ponsonby, who had whisked Vicky's precious letters away from Bertie several months earlier, hiding them in his own house, was able to keep them safe until 1928, when he edited and published them.

Looking back on her life, what was it that made her particularly susceptible to breast cancer? Early menstruation was certainly not a problem. According to her own account she kept very fit, making sure to take exercise, especially riding. Though she started motherhood by not breast-feeding her children, which was customary in her class at the time, she changed her mind and fed them herself after the first two. It seems there was no family history of breast cancer. So why did she develop it?

Perhaps her emotional history may be at least part of the reason: her struggle to champion good causes; her difficulties in trying to encourage liberal values and constitutional democracy in the face of Bismarck's autocracy; the terrible tragedy of her husband's short-lived reign and battle with throat cancer; her own suicidal depression, and particularly her struggles with her son Willy: his physical deformity, his defiance of her guidance and mentoring, and his betrayal of all she stood for. Her intellect and will were strong, her instincts entirely philanthropic, but her son, no doubt partly because of his own mental instability, presented her with problems that even she with all her wit could not solve. The deaths of her little boy Sigismund and her most promising son Waldemar were further tragedies. She was also frequently suppressed by male colleagues. It is hardly surprising that her immune system could not stand the strain.

Select Bibliography

Shrabani Basu:	*Victoria & Abdul: the extraordinary true story of the Queen's closest confidant* (The History Press, Stroud, 2010)
Hannah Pakula:	*An Uncommon Woman: the Empress Frederick: Daughter of Queen Victoria, Wife of the Crown Prince of Prussia, Mother of Kaiser Wilhelm* (Weidenfeld & Nicolson, London, 1996)
Andrew Roberts (ed.):	*Letters to Vicky: the correspondence between Queen Victoria and her daughter Victoria, Empress of Germany, 1858–1901* (Folio Society, London, 2011)

Helen Rappaport: *No Place for Ladies: the untold story of women in the Crimean War* (Aurum Press Ltd, London, 2007)

Cecil Woodham-Smith: *Queen Victoria: from her birth to the death of the Prince Consort* (Alfred A. Knopf, New York, 1972)

Notes

1.   Pakula, p. 67.
2.   Rappaport, p, 163.
3.   Pakula, p. 90.
4.   *ibid.*, p. 148.
5.   Roberts (ed.): *Letters to Vicky,* p. 109 (from the Crown Princess, Berlin, December 26, 1861).
6.   *ibid.*, p. 11 (from the Princess Royal, Berlin, February 16, 1858).
7.   *ibid.*, p. 126 (from the Crown Princess, Neues Palais, July 8, 1862).
8.   *ibid.*, p. 312 (from the Crown Princess, Bornstadt, May 28, 1870).
9.   Pakula, p. 270 (letter from Vicky to her mother).
10. Roberts (ed.): *Letters to Vicky,* p. 385 (from the Crown Princess, Berlin, April 26, 1873).
11. *ibid,*, p. 386 (from the Crown Princess, Vienna, May 8, 1873).
12. *ibid.*, pp. 505–6 (from the Crown Princess, Marlborough House, March 19, 1879).
13. *ibid.*, p. 507 (from the Crown Princess, Berlin, March 19, 1879).
14. *ibid.*, p. 507 (from the Crown Princess, Wiesbaden, April 10, 1879).
15. *ibid.*, p. 285 (from the Crown Princess, Berlin, April 10, 1869).
16. Pakula, p. 462.
17. Basu, p. 99.
18. Pakula, p. 510.
19. *ibid.*, p. 585.

Kate Greenaway

THE LIFE OF KATE GREENAWAY SPANS almost the same years as the Empress Vicky's: she was born on 17th March 1846, the second child of John and Elizabeth Greenaway, and died on 6th November 1901. But her social background was very different. Her parents were working-class, though her father's profession as a wood-engraver in London was in demand, and gradually the family climbed a few rungs up the social ladder. At the age of 24 John Greenaway was employed by Ebenezer Landells, who had been apprenticed to Thomas Bewick, the famous engraver, and he made speedy progress, becoming Landells' assistant. Soon afterwards he met Elizabeth Jones, daughter of a local butcher, and they married, settling down in 43 Southampton Street. They later moved to Britannia Street, where Kate was born.

Soon afterwards John Greenaway was commissioned to contribute engravings of illustrations to a new edition of Dickens' *Pickwick Papers*. His work increased, and he decided to move to 28 Napier Street, Hoxton, which had more room. But still he wanted freedom from distractions, and his family went to stay with relatives in Rolleston, Northamptonshire. Elizabeth became very ill, probably with influenza, and had to put Kate out to nurse. This could not have been good for either mother or child. Their separation from the father lasted almost two years, at the end of which John finished the work on *Pickwick Papers* and was able to welcome his family home. However, the *Pickwick* project was not a financial success, and John was then forced to accept any commission he could find: his future looked bleak. Another child was born, and the family struggled.

So Kate's infancy was difficult, though her mother was determined to care for her as best she could. The family moved to Hoxton New Town, part of Shoreditch. In 1851 Kate's mother opened a millinery shop, selling also children's dresses, and the family moved again into a flat in Islington, a lively area with shops and nearby pasture-land. The house also had a garden, which fascinated Kate. Her mother's business prospered (though her father's declined) and the family moved yet again: Kate began to learn middle-class respectability. But her mother was now working such long hours that she had little time for child-care, and 12-year-old Lizzie was left in charge of her younger siblings. According to her biographer Kate suffered from alternating 'high spirits and deep despair'[1] all her life: what we might term bipolar disorder. Here were the first signs of psychological issues that may later have had an effect on her immune system.

As a child, Kate made a huge collection of dolls and toys, and enjoyed holiday visits to Rolleston. One striking feature of this ancient village, mentioned in the Domesday Book, was the local habit of wearing old-fashioned clothes—rural smocks for the men and poke bonnets with frilly dresses for the women. These became a characteristic feature of Kate's artwork. She also revelled in the country sights and sounds, visits to markets and walks in the countryside, learning the names of wild flowers, and developing a somewhat idealized view of country life.

Kate was sent to various dame schools, none of which she liked. She also had private French and piano lessons. She was brought up very strictly by her mother and grandmother, in a puritanical religious tradition, which she later rebelled against. But she much enjoyed books, especially their illustrations. The children's writers Jane and Anne Taylor were her favourites. She learned much too from her favourite grandmother, Rebecca Jones, who entertained her with tea and scones on Sundays.

She continued to veer between deep depression and a lighter mood. Her father was a source of comfort and inspired her artistic efforts. She started evening classes at the Finsbury School of Art, and at the age of only 12 enrolled as a full-time student. The aim of this training was largely to fit pupils for designing fabrics, wallpapers and tiles; while some students found these lessons boring, Kate revelled in them. In the final stage of her six-year art course she received a national award for tile designs: a prestigious silver medal. She then went to the Female School of Art in South Kensington for another six years. Here she worked hard, but was very shy and made few friends. However, her work progressed well; she took part in life classes (though the models wore clothes), and sketched enthusiastically on her holidays in Rolleston. Her career in book illustration started with the frontispiece to *Infant Amusements or How to Make a Nursery Happy*. She also exhibited publicly in the Dudley Gallery.

Not satisfied with the clothed life class at her art school, she joined Heatherley's School of Art, where the models were nude, and men and women worked together. From there she progressed to the Slade School of Art, where again men and women attended the same class, and a free style was encouraged. By 1873 she left art college behind and struck out on her own. In the words of a poem she wrote at the time, she 'ventured on a new and lovely life'.[2] She undertook a great deal of work—mainly greeting cards and illustrations for children's books. Her earnings rose, and slowly she became a thoroughly successful professional artist. However, she suffered from nightmares about losing her father, who was of course her first mentor in the art world.

At this point Kate's two sisters (one older, one younger) both married, leaving just Kate and her brother Johnnie at home. Her work prospered and she took on a studio, so that she did not have to clear up at home at the end of every day. She persuaded street children to pose as models, in dresses of her own design.

Frederick Locker, a 57-year-old society gentleman who wrote lyric poetry, came into her life, introduced by her publisher Routledge, who thought Locker might offer helpful advice on Kate's verses and illustrations. In fact she did not accept his criticisms, but they remained friends for many years. Kate was now earning well from her work, especially from a new book of poems with illustrations, with the title *Under the Window (Pictures and Rhymes for Children)*, and was able to plan for her family to move to a new home in Hampstead (a fashionable London suburb)—a considerable step up the social scale. *Under the Window* did extremely well, the first edition of 20,000 selling out rapidly in time for Christmas 1879. The second edition sold 70,000, and within Kate's lifetime sales rose to 100,000.

This book launched her as an artist to be reckoned with, and enjoying a new independence. Stacy Marks was a strong influence on her, advising her to concentrate on book illustration and gain widespread appreciation, rather than trying to paint pictures, which could only reach a few customers.

Marks promoted her work among his friends: this led to contact with the art critic John Ruskin, who sent her a long letter containing much appreciative comment intertwined with a few critical remarks, and many questions. This was the beginning of a long friendship. What particularly drew them together was Kate's portrayal of pretty young girls, and Ruskin's obsession with 'girlies' (around the age of 9 or 10). Whether or not this penchant was ever acted out physically we do not know. But we do know that Ruskin's marriage to Effie Gray was dissolved after six years for non-consummation. (Effie went on to marry someone else.) It seems that he was unable to function sexually with his wife. Pre-pubertal girls attracted him, and Kate provided him with plenty of examples with her artwork, featuring largely 'girlies'.

The subsequent correspondence between Kate and Ruskin stretched over the next 20 years. She answered his first letter immediately, and so started the relationship that helped greatly with Kate's professional life, but had its serious problems too. Ruskin was a prophet of the Pre-Raphaelite school, which emphasized studies taken straight from nature. He took upon himself the role of artistic adviser, which gave him plenty of contact with her 'girlies'. Kate wanted a closer relationship, but Ruskin could not offer one: he seemed to fall short of any kind of sexual relationship with an adult woman.

Ruskin was a famous man, but a broken one, with a difficult past. Apart from his disastrous marriage, he had also been involved in a libel case: he had attacked paintings by James McNeill Whistler, and was sued. Costs were considerable and bankrupted Whistler, though he won the case, while Ruskin's costs were paid by public subscription. However, Ruskin's reputation was damaged, and his mental health affected. Formerly the first Slade Professor of Fine Art at Oxford University, in 1879 he resigned his Chair and retired to Brantwood, his house in Coniston in the Lake District, where he conducted a large correspondence, particularly with young women. He fell deeply in love with a girl of only nine, Rose la Touche, who came to him in 1858 for drawing lessons. When she was absent he found substitutes in a nearby girls' school, Winnington Hall. Finally at the age of 47 he proposed to Rose, now aged 17. Rose accepted him, but was not ready for physical love (probably like Ruskin himself), and broke off the engagement. She did not live for long afterwards, dying in 1875 at the age of only 27.

So Ruskin's relationship with Kate drew with it a whole history of love of young girls, which Kate was so good at illustrating. Here was her usefulness to Ruskin—reminding him constantly of his 'girlies'. Quite apart from that with Kate herself, he carried on a voluminous correspondence with other young women, and also some older women.

With Kate the correspondence became more and more intimate, though it was two years before they met. Kate was now in her mid-30s. During the next 20 years Kate would write to Ruskin over a thousand letters. Even modern texting would be hard put to it to compete. Her career flourished, with more invitations to provide drawings than she could accept, and meeting the eminent artists of the day, such as George du Maurier and Edward Burne-Jones. Her next publication, *Kate Greenaway's Birthday Book,* a miniature volume with verses by Mrs Sale Barker, was again a brilliant success, with a first edition of 50,000, French and German editions, and glowing reviews. Sadly, plagiarized versions of her books were also published, which greatly distressed her. But the *Birthday Book* continued selling well into the 20th century.

Ruskin now encouraged Kate to continue drawing and painting the 'girlies' he loved so much. But his own mental health was fragile, and in 1880 he was overcome with gloom and depression. Meanwhile Kate was demanding more and more attention from Ruskin, which he could not give. Another influence was Frederick Locker: he could not compete with Ruskin, but nevertheless offered Kate advice in artistic matters, which she was now happy to accept. Although he had a wife and children he hankered after a special relationship with Kate, and they did spend quite a bit of time together, mostly visiting London galleries and museums.

The poet Austin Dobson also admired her work. Perhaps the greatest honour for Kate was to meet Vicky the Crown Princess of Prussia at Buckingham Palace. She entertained the royal children and drew them pictures. Afterwards Kate continued to send her books and drawings to Vicky, and she received appreciative tokens in return.

By Christmas 1881 Ruskin had recovered from his depressive illness and was once more ready to advise Kate. He wrote to her with enthusiastic comments, though his depression returned soon afterwards. Ruskin now focused on Kate's work, trying to avoid depression, and even hoping to return to his Slade professorship at Oxford. He now planned to visit Kate herself for the first time. He was by then 63, and not very well. Kate was aged 36, plain of face and slow to smile. But her work enchanted Ruskin, and the meeting was a success. Thereafter Ruskin was a dominating influence on her life and work.

The next development was an invitation to Kate to come and stay at Brantwood with Ruskin. Joan Severn, his companion and housekeeper (a second cousin), was instructed to arrange the visit as quickly as possible, and for Kate, who had seldom ventured outside London, it was quite an adventure. She only intended to stay for a fortnight, but in fact she stayed for over a month. The setting by Coniston Water was of great beauty, and Ruskin's possessions — books, pictures, sculptures, manuscripts, together with the beautiful house and gardens — enchanted Kate. Part of the time she was there Ruskin worked on his Oxford lecture on her work, entitled 'In Fairyland': its publication ran to 35 pages. Its thesis was that Kate was in the first rank of artists, ancient and modern. The lecture was very popular: it was delivered three times and subsequently printed privately. Kate was now more or less obliged to follow Ruskin's way, and Ruskin became even more emotionally attached to her. While appreciating Kate's technical skill, modern art-lovers may perhaps not put her quite so high in the artistic pantheon as Ruskin did.

'Darling Katie,' he wrote, 'I'm thinking of you every day and a great part of the day long, whenever I get out into the fields more and more, anxious everyday that you should resolve on summer's work of utter veracity — drawing no matter what, *but* as it *is*.'[3]

The correspondence became more and more intense. Ruskin encouraged Kate to visit Scarborough, which she did, though she only stayed a week. Ruskin chided her with not having stayed long enough, and then bombarded her with letters. He could not have enough pictures of young girls, and continued to offer Kate artistic guidance, but their letters were also full of endearments, like love letters.

In between pleasing Ruskin with drawings of 'girlies' Kate tried to keep up her flow of publications, which were now much in demand. But her feelings for Ruskin became stronger and stronger, and in 1884 the couple exchanged letters almost daily. Ruskin even sent telegrams when he felt the matter was urgent. He also sent her a complete set of his books, bound in white leather.

In 1886 Ruskin spent a month in London, and Kate saw as much of him as she could. She invited him to sit for his portrait, and this emboldened her to speak of love. This only made Ruskin cross, but Kate's feelings grew all the same, even though Ruskin's mental health was wavering. She was in a state of torture, unable to put Ruskin out of her mind.

Here we might pause and consider what effect this relationship must have had on Kate's general health and immune system. There is no doubt that Kate was passionately in love with Ruskin, but that Ruskin himself, though he had perhaps once had similar feelings, and though he was still fond of Kate and keen to be her artistic mentor, could not now look upon her as a lover. At 38 he found her unattractive and old maidish (though he was so much older). He played games with her feelings, and often hurt her cruelly. She wrote him poems and persevered in her efforts to get close to him: he encouraged her letters, and visited her studio in London, but became ill so that their visits to galleries had to be cancelled. He returned to Brantwood and put Kate off for months, finally inviting her again on 6th August 1884. But this visit too was put off: Joan Severn was unwell, and could not offer hospitality. She was also worried about Ruskin's mental health.

That Christmas (1884) Kate received a Christmas present from Vicky, the Crown Princess of Prussia. Her publications were still proving popular, and she was earning enough to make possible a move to Hampstead. But her relationship with Ruskin was still difficult. Locker extended her circle by introducing her to famous people such as Robert Browning and Tennyson family members. But her one real obsession was with Ruskin. Throughout 1884 she wrote passionate letters to him. Ruskin enjoyed the attention but did not reciprocate. Kate became more and more depressed and discouraged. However, her move with her parents to Hampstead, on 15th February 1885, seems to have lifted her spirits. The house was large and spacious, on three floors, with a huge studio. She loved Hampstead, and the Heath was constantly inspiring. Kate's brother Johnnie was now sub-editor of the *Journal of the Chemistry Society*. Her father was still working at his engraving, but not very successfully. Kate worked hard and systematically, and continued to write to Ruskin, who finally resigned his Oxford professorship over the question of vivisection, to which he was opposed.

Kate's next visit to Brantwood was on 17th April 1885: she travelled with Joan Severn. However, the visit was not a success: the weather was poor and Kate was miserable, unable to please Ruskin with her drawings of flowers and stones. Later that year Ruskin suffered his most serious episode of mental ill health so far, and Kate's *Marigold Garden* was less successful than her previous publications. Kate was now conflicted between producing the illustrations that she knew would sell, and the work that Ruskin wanted her to produce. She started work on a joint book with him, on Beauty and the Beast, but the project fizzled out. She spent much time in her new garden in Hampstead: flowers were important to her. She cultivated an informal gardening style, with no pruning, and frogs imported from the Hampstead Ponds to keep down the insects.

Her next book was a story by an American writer, Bret Harte, with the title *The Queen of the Pirate Isle*. She exhausted herself working on it. She was hoping to visit Brantwood, but Ruskin suffered another serious episode of madness — 'more terrible than any yet', he reported.[4] He recovered yet again, and became his usual repentant self. But in 1887 he invited Kate to Brantwood once more, and the visit went well, even though Ruskin was in poor health.

Kate's next project was a new edition of Robert Browning's 'Pied Piper of Hamelin', for which she gained the poet's approval. She struggled with perspective: her brother Johnnie and her father both tried to help her, but Johnnie realized that her problem was actually poor eyesight. In spite of this she persevered with the exercises in perspective sent to her by Ruskin. She also consulted her doctor, Elizabeth Garrett Anderson, who lived near her in Hampstead and prescribed a medicine to be taken nine times a day. Although we have very few of Kate's letters to Ruskin, from this time he did start keeping them in his 'Greenaway drawer', and the nature of her feelings for him is embarrassingly clear. She sent the following letter after the death of one of his secretaries, which was a terrible blow to him.

My Dear. My Dear Dinie — I am very sorry to hear your sad news and sorry too, for the shock to you, just now — when you are not well — it is very sad — how often it seems to happen — to people who are — not strong. — I'm very sorry for All of you… may all things bless and Comfort you Dear. With all my love. Katie.[5]

That year Queen Victoria's golden jubilee celebrations were a great attraction, and Kate took her young niece Catherine (a frequent model) and nephew Eddie Dadd on excursions to visit them. But her main emotional life was with Ruskin, who recognized her sacrifices. He wrote:

My poor Katie — you don't know what a blessing it is to you — that you have done nothing to repent of — but have done for Father and Mother and brother and for me, every dutiful and loving deed — I am in a fearful fit of remorse just now for all the selfishness and anger and extravagance of my life.[6]

Kate paid another visit to Ruskin, this time in Sandgate, and now she was shocked by his demeanour: emotionally erratic and bordering on madness. Back home her work was less successful artistically: it was done largely for the money. But she renewed her friendship with an old art-school acquaintance, Helen Paterson, who was highly regarded by Ruskin; he even advised Kate to learn from her. In 1889 she was elected a member of the Royal Institute of Painters in Watercolour, and with Helen Allingham spent several days around Amersham and Chesham in Buckinghamshire, painting in country lanes.

Meanwhile Ruskin's mental health was deteriorating again, and Kate's visit to Brantwood was cancelled. Her own depression came back, accompanied by fog in Hampstead. She needed to make money and even accepted commissions for advertising illustrations. But her artistic development still had a new furrow to plough. 'A lonely soul, I am ever alone,' she wrote in a poem around this time. In January 1890 Ruskin became seriously ill, indeed delirious. But Kate wrote intense poems about her feelings *for* him, if not *to* him. She too suffered from depression, but derived comfort from another gift from the Empress Frederick — in return for her Christmas almanac.

In August 1890 Kate's father John Greenaway died aged 73 after pneumonia, nursed by Kate, who by then was also supporting him financially. His work was respected and admired by colleagues, but his business had been going downhill for years. Kate was devastated by his death, but she plucked up courage and held her first solo exhibition at the Fine Art Society in February 1891. It was a success, artistically and commercially, but Kate had sacrificed some of her favourite pictures. She went back to work, and tired herself out, but recuperated during the autumn in Bournemouth as a guest of the Hon. Gerald Ponsonby, an art connoisseur, and his wife, who to some extent took the place of Frederick Locker. Lady Maria Ponsonby was especially helpful and sympathetic.

Kate was now suffering repeated bouts of painful neuralgia or rheumatism, and in September 1892 also had to nurse her mother without the support of her brother, who was away on holiday. Her mother improved, and Ruskin's health also grew better, but her own health deteriorated. She went for a holiday with Frederick Locker (now Locker-Lampson) and his children in Cromer. She enjoyed the warm hospitality, but the hot sea-water baths did not help with her pain, and it grew worse. Back in Hampstead she recovered somewhat, and made plans for further exhibitions, including her one and only in Glasgow. But by winter 1893 Kate was worn out, and with serious money worries; her mother was still ill, her brother also not well. By 1894 Kate was worrying that Ruskin would not recognize her now that her hair was turning grey; she was having fainting fits; her exhibition in January 1894 did not break new ground, and sales were disappointing.

In February Kate's mother died, aged 81, watched by her daughter, now lonely, inconsolable and distressed for months. She worked little, but accepted invitations to social occasions. Eventually she agreed to work for an American magazine, the *Ladies' Home Journal,* whose editor was visiting England. Lewis Carroll and Florence Nightingale refused to contribute to his journal, and so did Kate initially, but he persisted in pursuing her, and finally ran her to earth in her Hampstead house. She found working for him was actually easy money.

She returned to Brantwood to visit Ruskin, finding him much more frail. Back home she entertained her niece and nephew Catherine and Eddie Dadd over Christmas 1895, but on their departure felt lonely. Another blow was the death of Frederick Locker-Lampson. A further visit to Brantwood in October proved difficult: it was the last time she saw Ruskin.

Kate's ability to draw and paint was now severely affected by the pain of her neuralgia. She drifted towards Impressionism (technically easier perhaps?). Her loneliness continued, and she felt disillusioned in her career, struggling mainly to make money. She needed a confidante, and found one in Violet Dickinson, a spinster of 31, six foot two in height, with interests in literature, bookbinding and music. The relationship became intimate and even passionate, though probably not actually sexual. However, Violet brought out a more fun-loving Kate, less reserved and dowdy than before. Reluctantly she went on designing almanacs, which were a sure money-spinner, but this year's was her last. She now turned to verse, particularly to give voice to her loneliness, and her enduring love for Ruskin.

In 1897 the Queen's 60th Jubilee year was celebrated, and this was an opportunity for feminists to publicize their campaign to be taken seriously as artists, workers and citizens. Kate, although promoted as a successful woman, was embarrassed by the 'shrieking sisterhood', and did not believe that women were held back by prejudice. She did not support 'Votes for Women'. She felt that she had been fairly treated as a woman artist. She even wrote to Violet Dickinson:

> I would far rather exhibit my things with them and take my true place which must be lower than so many of theirs. For I fear we can only hope to do — what men can do. It is sad but I fear it is so. They have more ability.[7]

But of course Kate had in fact been very successful, and had supported her own parents in a way that any man would have envied. She had adroitly climbed up the social scale, ending up in a large and beautiful house in a fashionable Hampstead street, without the support of a husband. Kate's problem now was to make enough money to keep going, which meant painting pictures that would sell, not necessarily those she wanted to produce. At the same time she was something of a celebrity, asked to comment on current events much in the style of modern radio or television. 'I have at last had to give up answering letters', she told Ruskin.[8]

Kate's brother Johnnie was a source of concern, as he also suffered from bouts of depression, and went off to Switzerland for treatment. In February 1898 Kate put on an exhibition at the Fine Art Society, of portraits, landscapes, and illustrations. Sadly the weather was bad and the attendance poor. The exhibition was not a success — her work was now out of fashion.

At this time Kate's religious views — or lack of them — came to the fore when she was staying with the Locker-Lampsons at Cromer, and played croquet with the children while her hostess was at church. She was severely chastised for her sinful behaviour, but Kate refused to change her ways, asserting that 'I never can, never shall see it is more religious to sit in a hot church trying to listen to a commonplace sermon than looking at a beautiful sky…'[9]

Kate now turned her hand to portrait painting, in oils — which was more likely to be remunerative, but offered serious technical challenges in contrast with watercolour. She also began an autobiography, which did not get very far. On 20th January 1900 Ruskin died, after influenza. He was buried at Coniston, not Westminster Abbey, though a service was held there as well. Kate's feelings, long bottled up, could now be expressed in a letter to Joan Severn: 'I am so dreadfully sorry when I feel I might have given him more pleasure.' She planned to design his tomb, 'all girls and children and angels,'[10] but the idea came to nothing. More commissions followed, but she struggled to fulfil her contracts through a season of illness — influenza and sharp chest pains. She wrote passionate verses to Ruskin, and Joan Severn, who was sorting through his papers, asked for permission to use some of her letters in the biographical section of a library edition of his works—suitably edited. Kate had of course kept all Ruskin's letters to her, and was only too pleased to be associated with him in any memoirs.

Kate had been told in November 1899 that she had breast cancer and needed an operation, but postponed it until July 1900. When it finally took place the disease had metastasized and she had a limited time to live. Money worries added to her distress—she had little wherewith to pay the doctor. But she confessed to no one the real nature of her illness: breast cancer was something shameful and unmentionable. Her doctor's prescription was clearly meant to alleviate her pain, consisting of medicine nine times a day, beef tea, eggs and milk, and considerable quantities of alcohol. In fact she managed quite well on this regime, even doing some work, and it was not until the following July that the pain returned with full force, as the cancer had spread to the spine. It then travelled to her lungs, and on 6th November 1901, during thick fog in Hampstead, Kate died, aged 55.

Her wish, unusual for the time, was to be cremated, which was done in Woking, and her ashes returned to Hampstead, to be buried next to her parents in the family plot. Kate's reputation had spread to France and Germany, where her favourite child model, her nephew Eddie Dadd, now lived, and also America, where many articles appraising her work appeared. A biography was written by Marion Spielmann, but this was disliked by her family and was not a success at the time. However, Kate's own work continued to be honoured and reprinted. In 1955 the Kate Greenaway Medal was established, to be awarded annually to a British illustrator of children's books. Her Hampstead house received a commemorative plaque. Her works still command high prices.

So what was it in her life that might have precipitated her breast cancer? At the age of 55 she was very likely menopausal, a common time for breast cancer to develop. She had never married or had children: another risk factor. But her emotional life must have put a great deal of stress on her immune system: her frustrating relationship with Ruskin, passionate but never consummated, must surely have played its part. Since her disease was diagnosed late and her surgery postponed, her creativity (which was considerable) was inevitably extinguished. But also we might guess that Ruskin himself, with his continual requests for pictures of his 'girlies', might have turned away her creative spirit from what it otherwise might have developed into. Her conviction that men were better than women, even though her own achievement was outstanding, may also have contributed to the foiling of her creative fire.

Select Bibliography

Rodney Engen: *Kate Greenaway: A Biography* (Macdonald, London, 1981)

M.H. Spielmann and G.S. Layard: *The Life and Work of Kate Greenaway* (Adam Charles Black, London, 1905, new edition Bracken Books, London, 1986)

Tim Hilton: *John Ruskin: the Later Years* (Yale University Press, New Haven and London, 2000)

John Ruskin: *Selected Writings*, edited with an Introduction and Notes by Dinah Birch (Oxford World's Classics, Oxford University Press, 2004)

Kate Greenaway: *Kate Greenaway's Birthday Book with verses by Mrs Sale Barker* (Frederick Warne, London, n.d.)

Robert Browning: *The Pied Piper of Hamelin*, with illustrations by Kate Greenaway (Everyman's Library, Random House, London, 1993)

Notes

1. Engen, p. 15.
2. Engen, p. 44 (chapter heading).
3. Letter of 15th June 1883: Pierpont Morgan Library (quoted in Engen, p. 92).
4. Letter of 24th August 1886: Pierpont Morgan Library (quoted in Engen, p. 141).
5. Quoted in Engen, p. 148.
6. Spielmann and Layard, p. 252.
7. *ibid.*, p. 214.
8. *ibid.*, p. 211.
9. Engen, p. 208.
10. Spielmann and Layard, p. 23.

Vanessa Bell

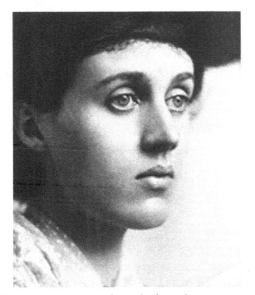

VANESSA WAS BORN ON 11TH MAY 1879, the eldest child of Leslie and Julia Stephen. Both her parents had been widowed before they remarried; Julia already had three children, and Leslie had one. The family grew rapidly, with Julian Thoby born a year later, Virginia in 1882, and Adrian in 1883. As the oldest of this new family, Vanessa took on the role of caring for her younger siblings. Thoby shared lessons with her: these were mostly given by their mother Julia, until Thoby was sent away to a preparatory school. Vanessa continued to be taught by her mother.

At this point her relationship with Virginia was strengthened, though Virginia cruelly nicknamed her 'The Saint' (the household was agnostic). Living in London close to Hyde Park, the children played there regularly, and sailed their boats on the Round Pond in Kensington Gardens. Their father Leslie Stephen was Editor of the *Dictionary of National Biography*, a task that grew increasingly burdensome until he resigned in 1891. But he was a devoted father, and took his family on regular summer holidays walking in St Ives in Cornwall. Here Vanessa started to draw, instructed by John Ruskin's *The Elements of Drawing*. Even in childhood it was clear that Vanessa wanted to be an artist, and Virginia a writer: rivalry was therefore unnecessary.

Vanessa's mother Julia had been through a rough time before marrying Leslie Stephen: she was pregnant with her third child at the age of 24 when her first husband died suddenly. Finally she had eight children to look after, and constantly cared for others as well, particularly her mother in her last illness (though the household boasted several servants). But she also had literary tastes to match those of her husband, and encouraged domestic music. She was much loved, but sadly died at the age of only 49, after influenza followed by rheumatic fever.

Her husband was devastated, and Vanessa at the age of only 16 took over something of her maternal role. She continued to study art, taught by Ebenezer Cooke, who directed her towards Ruskin's methods. Although Leslie Stephen himself was not interested in art, he took pains to engage the best tuition for Vanessa, and was even something of a feminist, saying:

What I chiefly hold is that women ought to be as well educated as men, indeed a very great deal better than men are now... I hate to see so many women's lives wasted simply because they have not been trained well enough to take an independent interest in any study or to be able to work efficiently at any profession.[1]

In 1896 at the age of 17 Vanessa started classes at an art school in South Kensington. Meanwhile George Duckworth, Julia Stephen's oldest son from her first marriage, took over as head of the family, as Leslie Stephen was becoming increasingly frail. It seems that George was inclined to fondle his half-sisters inappropriately — particularly Virginia, whom he approached at night in her bedroom. Vanessa did not like it, and it seriously upset Virginia, who shortly afterwards had her first bout of mental illness.

Then Stella, Julia Stephen's oldest daughter by her first marriage, who had been caring for all the family on both sides since Julia's death, herself died early, and Vanessa had to take complete care of her younger siblings, at a time when she herself was only just 'coming out' and attending London functions. She was obliged to take her place, aged 18, as mistress of the house. This involved receiving a variety of callers, including Henry James, Sir Alfred Lyall and Lady Ritchie, we are told by Violet Dickinson, who became a family friend, and also provides a link in our breast cancer story with Kate Greenaway. Violet was a single gentlewoman: over six foot tall, and known for her generosity and good works.

Vanessa's entry into society had been curtailed by mourning, but now her half-brother George Duckworth insisted on escorting her to various functions, though she went reluctantly, and rarely enjoyed them. She also had to run the household, holding regular tea parties for the benefit of her father: she was obliged to return home by 4.30 pm every day to do this. She also had to submit weekly accounts to him: he seems to have been unreasonably tyrannical on the subject.

It appears that Vanessa's first emotional entanglement was with Jack, widower of Stella, Vanessa's half-sister. At this juncture in England such a marriage would have been illegal, so if Vanessa's feelings went beyond the merely 'fond', this was her first experience of her emotions carrying her outside socially acceptable norms. It was not to be the last. Vanessa's professional career as an artist took a new turn with her entry into the Royal Academy Painting School in 1901. Here she studied drawing and anatomy, and took part in life classes, though these were segregated until 1903. The Pre-Raphaelites, promoted by Ruskin, were beginning to give way to the style of John Singer Sargent, who taught Vanessa at the Royal Academy: he in his turn was influenced by Monet. This led to Vanessa's fascination with the Impressionists.

However, things were changing: Clive Bell, a Cambridge friend of her brother Thoby, paid a visit which eventually resulted in a more intimate friendship. In the meantime, in 1902 her father was diagnosed with abdominal cancer, and caring for him dominated Vanessa's life until his death in February 1904. The last stages of such an illness can be extremely stressful for both patient and carer, even with the help of servants, which Vanessa certainly had. To be able to carry on her work as an artist she set up a studio at home, since her visits to the Academy were now restricted by her domestic duties, and it was only her father's death that released her from what had become a heavy burden.

The Stephens, now released from caring for their father, were able to take holidays, and in April 1904 they went to Venice, which totally enchanted Vanessa, and then Florence, where she met Violet Dickinson. On the way home they stayed in Paris and were entertained by Clive Bell and his friends, but soon after arriving in London Virginia had her first serious mental breakdown (perhaps precipitated by her father's death), during which she attempted suicide. Once again Vanessa was forced into the role of carer, though Violet Dickinson also helped.

Vanessa now planned to move from Hyde Park Gate to Bloomsbury, which was near the Slade School of Art, though at the time not particularly fashionable. The move to 46 Gordon Square was achieved in 1904, and signified freedom from the old ways, especially since George Duckworth was now married and living separately, with his wife Margaret. Vanessa was now fully occupied in furnishing and arranging her new house, to her own taste.

Thoby Stephen moved into the house and began to hold Thursday evening 'at homes'. Vanessa writes:

> Thoby, not long down from Cambridge and now reading for the Bar, began to gath-
> er round him such of his Cambridge friends as were also starting life in London. It
> seemed to him a good plan to be at home one evening a week and though I do not think
> that it had at first occurred to him to include his sisters in the arrangement, still there
> they were.[2]

These friends included Clive Bell, and were crucial in forming the Bloomsbury group. Clive had attended Marlborough College before Cambridge, and had a wealthy *nouveau riche* background. At Cambridge he had been a member of the 'Midnight' play-reading club, together with Lytton Strachey and Leonard Woolf. He had been seduced about five years before, aged 18, by a neighbour, Mrs Raven-Hill, but the affair seems to have been purely physical. When Clive began to see Vanessa regularly, he found she had not only physical beauty but also intellectual and artistic distinction.

Vanessa was now 26. Clive fell heavily in love with her, and in August 1905 proposed, but was refused. It is perhaps unsurprising that after so many years of domestic commitment to her father and her sister, both of whom were very needy, the idea of being tied down in marriage was unacceptable. At last Vanessa was free to pursue her career as an artist, without family commitments. She founded the Friday Club, drawing together artists, as well as her brothers Thoby and Adrian. Eventually the club put on impressive exhibitions, in the years before the First World War. It linked together disparate elements, both the French Impressionist tradition and the more conservative British one. Socially it was still a time when young women of Vanessa's class could not go out unaccompanied: Edwardian standards of behaviour applied. But the Thursday evenings and Friday Club were opportunities for social as well as artistic liberation for Vanessa, as the meetings were in her own home.

Vanessa was now pursuing her artistic career with passion, and refused Clive Bell's second proposal in July 1906, after which Vanessa, Virginia and Violet Dickinson went on holiday in Greece. However, Vanessa fell ill on the journey, possibly as a consequence of the continual anxiety and responsibility for others that had exhausted her in the previous few years. She returned home to find her brother Thoby also ill, with typhoid, and he died shortly after Vanessa's return. Clive had been in and out of the house attempting to care for him. When he proposed to Vanessa yet again, he was accepted. This time she was genuinely happy: to some extent Clive filled the gap left by Thoby's death, and they spent long hours talking to each other. They were married in St Pancras Register Office in 1907.

To begin with their marriage seems to have been very successful, both sexually and in other respects. The Bells took over 46 Gordon Square, while Virginia and Adrian moved into another Bloomsbury address: 29 Fitzroy Square. A new play-reading group was formed, the first work chosen being Vanbrugh's *The Relapse,* a notoriously bawdy play. The more conventional friends fell away, and the Bloomsbury group evolved into what it became famous for, a set of unconventional artists with 'modern' manners. Vanessa took delight in being the equal of any man in her conversation: this was a new take on feminism.

The Bloomsbury group, formed mainly of intellectuals, several educated at Cambridge, took as its tenet a quotation from the philosopher G.E. Moore: 'personal affection and aesthetic enjoyments include *all* the greatest, and *by far* the greatest, goods we can imagine'.[3] Desmond MacCarthy (a member of the Cambridge Apostles, the intellectual secret society) joined the group, and Leonard Woolf, also an Apostle and a Jew recently risen from a background of shopkeepers into the professional class. As for Vanessa, she could now talk freely and shake off her Victorian upbringing: with four servants, she could draw and paint, and sell her work; but still she could not vote.

Vanessa was soon pregnant and delivered her firstborn, Julian, without much trouble on 4th February 1908. Among the new visitors to Gordon Square was the economist John Maynard Keynes, also a Cambridge graduate and now working at the India Office. Vanessa and Clive visited the Bell family in Seend, Wiltshire, where Clive's father was now regarded as 'Squire Bell'. Here Vanessa met Mrs Raven-Hill, who gave her useful information about contraception: Vanessa was ignorant of her former role as Clive's mistress.

While Julian's birth delighted Vanessa, Clive did not react so well. He took to sleeping in a separate room to escape the child's cries, and also began to flirt with

Virginia, much to Vanessa's distress. Once more she managed her pain, as she had always done. Meanwhile, in 1909 Clive resumed his affair with Mrs Raven-Hill, which continued until 1914. Vanessa worked at her painting, and in spite of Clive's flirtations, the couple remained close.

At this point Lady Ottoline Morrell, the well-known society hostess, made overtures to Vanessa, clearly wishing to bring the Bloomsbury group within her sphere of influence: she was having an affair with the artist Augustus John at the time. Lady Ottoline remained on the fringe of the group for some time. Another person Vanessa met during this period was the distinguished art critic Roger Fry, whose wife Helen was subject to mental illness: in 1910 she was confined to an asylum. Her own sister Virginia also had another mental breakdown, and Vanessa and Clive tried to help, taking her on holiday with them, though later Virginia was admitted to a private nursing home.

Vanessa was now pregnant again, and closer to Clive. On 10th August 1910 she gave birth to another boy, eventually named Quentin. Back in Gordon Square, she was able to see a ground-breaking exhibition of Post-Impressionists — Manet, Cézanne, Gauguin, Van Gogh — organized by Roger Fry, and somewhat shocking to an English audience. Vanessa was bowled over. 'Freedom was given to one to be oneself and that to the young is the most exciting thing that can happen'.[4] The freedom of expression illustrated by the Post-Impressionists was of course much valued by the Bloomsbury group, and this exhibition signalled, in Vanessa's words, 'a sizzle of excitement, new relationships, new ideas, different and intense emotions...'[5]

Roger himself was a key figure in this movement, and he became closer to Vanessa when he offered sympathy and understanding as her new baby failed to gain weight. He also accompanied Clive and Vanessa on a trip to Turkey in 1911, which was packed full of excitement. However, Vanessa was still not well, and suffered a miscarriage and total physical breakdown on the way back in Greece. She was also mentally unstable. Roger, with the experience of his own wife's mental illness, took charge and nursed her back to health. Afterwards Vanessa visited Roger in Guildford, and slowly they grew closer, until it became a passionate affair. Clive could hardly object, since he too had been playing away for years. Moreover, Vanessa's relationship with Roger gave her a new inspiration as a painter.

In summer 1911 Virginia married Leonard Woolf, and Clive seems to have stopped flirting with her. Somehow Vanessa kept her relationship with him on a sound footing, in spite of her affair with Roger. Besides being associated with the Bloomsbury area of London, the group also sought a country retreat. The first of these was at Asheham, near Lewes, in Sussex, which Vanessa and her family and friends visited during the years 1912–14.

The next project associated with the group was the second Post-Impressionist Exhibition, which Roger Fry prepared for autumn 1912 at the Grafton Galleries.

It included work by both Vanessa and Duncan Grant, who was now working with Vanessa at Asheham. Other artists represented included Matisse, Picasso, Derain and Vlaminck. The Post-Impressionist standpoint was that adopted by Vanessa for the rest of her life. It was articulated in the book *Art*, written by Clive Bell, but drawing also on Roger Fry's ideas, and published in 1914. Vanessa acted as both copy-editor and proof-reader.

At this point Vanessa grew closer to Duncan Grant, who was six years younger than her and engaged in homosexual relationships, not least with her brother Adrian and formerly John Maynard Keynes. A current partner was David Garnett. In the Bloomsbury group, although homosexuality was still illegal (for men), it was fairly common among the Cambridge graduates who were members. Vanessa now had serious feelings for three men: her husband Clive, her lover Roger, and also for Duncan. At the same time she was drawing away from Virginia, though she was called on to help when her sister attempted suicide. The war in 1914 brought dilemmas for the men in the group: should they enlist or not? Asheham was a convenient retreat out of danger of war, and conscription had not yet arrived. Another refuge was Eleanor House, West Wittering, on the Sussex coast. But Vanessa's two young boys remained in London, in the care of a nurse, and attending a local school. They visited West Wittering at Easter, much to Vanessa's delight.

Vanessa's private life was extremely complicated, but her painting did not seem to suffer: rather the reverse. Later that year she returned to the Sussex coast with Clive and the children, renting a house at Bosham. But Clive too was now pursuing someone else — Mary Hutchinson. He also wrote a pacifist pamphlet, 'Peace at Once', which drew considerable opposition. Various other friends took up a pacifist position. David Garnett had been working in France, with the Friends' War Victims' Relief Fund. (As a child, he had a cloak made of rabbit skin and thus received the nickname 'Bunny'.) Duncan too was attracted by an invitation to Paris, but at Dieppe was accused by officials of being a 'pacifist anarchist', and to avoid imprisonment returned home. So all Vanessa's closest companions were of pacifist sympathies.

In 1916 conscription was introduced, for all single men in England without dependants between ages 18 and 41. Clive Bell sat on a committee that looked at what could be done for conscientious objectors. Those engaged in essential manual labour would be exempt from conscription, so both Duncan and Bunny did just that — on a farm near Wessett, where Vanessa's family had now moved. Their farming was somewhat amateurish, but they hoped to be safe from conscription, and Vanessa could continue her painting.

However, Duncan and Bunny had to seek farm work elsewhere as the Central Tribunal decided they were not exempt if they were self-employed. Vanessa now found another farmhouse, Charleston, only four miles away, where Bunny and Duncan could also be employed. This house turned out to be a great success, and the country retreat for the Bloomsbury group for many years to come. It is now a tourist attraction, with a shop and gallery, workshops and events, and even a festival. Vanessa lived there permanently until the end of the war, and then until 1939 it was only a holiday home, coming into its own again with the Second World War.

Duncan and Vanessa were only tenants, but with the permission of the owner did a great deal of redecoration. Her husband Clive was now living elsewhere, and her present partner was Duncan. Financially she was secure, with an allowance from Clive and her own income from investments as well as her painting. She also provided many illustrations and cover designs for the Hogarth Press, founded in 1917 by Leonard and Virginia Woolf.

Visitors to Charleston included John Maynard Keynes, E.M. Forster, Lytton Strachey, Roger Fry, and Virginia and Leonard Woolf. Maynard took over the lease of 46 Gordon Square in 1916, though it remained a town house for the residents of Charleston. Vanessa set up a small school at home for her two boys and two young girls. Life at Charleston was thoroughly unconventional, with Vanessa 'living like an old hen wife among ducks, chickens and children' according to Virginia.[6] Quentin comments: 'As a wartime refuge Charleston had much to recommend it. With a farm next door, a garden full of produce and a countryside rich in game, we did not starve.'[7]

In Charleston emotional entanglements were complicated. Vanessa and Duncan were in a relationship, but so were Duncan and Bunny, who shared a bedroom. Bunny also wanted to sleep with Vanessa, but was rejected. Soon after, Roger and Clive arrived on a visit, so all three of Vanessa's lovers were together. In April 1918 she conceived a child by Duncan, but Clive agreed to assume parenthood. Keeping all these relationships together but apart must have been somewhat tricky. Vanessa was characterized by Virginia as mysterious and romantic: her calm exterior masking her inner vulnerability. Here we see the signs of the personality that may have contributed to her final cancer: an ability to cover up inner torment and stifle early trauma. But she was able to use her art as sublimation and therapy: the cancer was not to strike for many years to come.

Vanessa's baby girl was born on Christmas Day 1918, at home in Charleston. Servants came and went, and the local doctor gave bad advice when the baby failed to gain weight. But Vanessa changed to a woman doctor under whose care the baby flourished. She was finally named Angelica. It was now safe to return to London and resume living in Bloomsbury, where the group was now associated with other writers such as T.S. Eliot, the Sitwells, Aldous Huxley and Raymond Mortimer, and the Memoir Club was founded; it continued to meet until the death of Clive Bell in 1964.

The First World War had opened up new opportunities for women, and finding reliable servants was now a problem for Vanessa. But she managed, and started painting again. A guest at Charleston was John Maynard Keynes, who wrote *The Economic Consequences of the Peace,* a controversial account of the Paris Peace Conference, at Charleston in August–September 1919. In spring 1920 Vanessa went on holiday with Maynard and Duncan to Italy. They had a wonderful time, stopping in Paris on the way home. Meanwhile Angelica continued to be regarded as the daughter of Clive, which left Duncan to have a playful, brotherly relationship with her. Angelica herself tells the story of how this deceit had a long-term impact on her development in her autobiographical study *Deceived with Kindness.*

In 1921 Vanessa, Duncan, and the three children spent an idyllic time in St Tropez, from October to January: the two boys received lessons in French, but in other subjects Julian's education by now was seriously lacking. On their return home he was sent to a Quaker boarding school, Leighton Park, while Quentin attended a preparatory school. Vanessa spent some more time in Paris, leaving Angelica with a nurse; she then held her first one-woman show, at Percy Moore Turner's Independent Gallery, and sold several works, though there were no reviews.

Personal relationships in the Bloomsbury set were always complex. At this point John Maynard Keynes, who had been very helpful to Vanessa, proposed marriage to his mistress Lydia Lopokova, a ballerina whose portrait Vanessa painted: but this meant that Maynard was no longer so intimately connected with Bloomsbury, and Lydia herself was not popular with the group. Vanessa's work during the 1920s reflected her increased interest in all things French and Italian: she accepted commissions for interior decoration as well as pictures. The Bloomsbury group's interest in interior design dated from the foundation of the Omega workshops, started by Roger Fry after the second Post-Impressionist exhibition, in June 1913. 'His idea was to couple Post-Impressionism in fine art with home decoration… Omega designs were bold, focusing on colour and form.'[8]

A studio was now added to the house at Charleston, and life there was all that could be wished for, though electric light and telephones were still to come. Vanessa organized a summer school for children (including her own), for which she provided art lessons. Duncan was now her constant companion; the two boys delighted in editing their *Charleston Bulletin*, which chronicled important events and gossip in satirical style. Roger Fry, on a visit in 1926, commented:

> It really is an almost ideal family based as it is on adultery and mutual forbearance with Clive the deceived husband and me the abandoned lover. It really is rather a triumph of reasonableness over the conventions.[9]

Vanessa's career as an artist now accelerated, with a triumphant show in Bond Street in February 1930 devoted entirely to her art and well reviewed by John Piper. She and Duncan also exhibited decorative work, which was very popular and sold well.

By this time it is probable that her sexual relationship with Duncan was no longer active, and she tolerated his homosexual liaisons. At the centre of Vanessa's life then there was a passion that was inevitably one-sided and could not be fully reciprocated. But she made the best of it and made a point of forging good relations with Duncan's various lovers. In 1934 Vanessa and Duncan set up house at La Bergère in Cassis, near Aix-en-Provence, which became a second Charleston. They spent a great deal of time painting.

Vanessa's life, though busy, yet had an underlying streak of unhappiness: how could she keep all her lovers happy — and indeed herself? The only way out was to paint. Her children were now growing up, and the youngest, Angelica, was sent to boarding school. She could now focus fully on her painting.

On 4th February 1930 there opened a one-woman show of Vanessa's work at the Cooling Galleries in London: sales were good. But at the same time Vanessa was extremely anxious on account of another threat to her relationship with Duncan, a Jewish American/Russian bisexual artist called George Bergen. Duncan even took George down to Charleston in Vanessa's absence. Vanessa wrote: 'Duncan dear, I don't want you to come back — until you come back altogether.'[10] Again she found therapy in painting. Duncan acknowledged that he loved both George and Vanessa.

During the 1930s in spite of economic belt-tightening there were many visitors to Charleston. As well as painting and drawing, Vanessa's work included designs for pottery and china, and other decorative art, sets for ballet, and indeed portraits. Duncan and Vanessa broke with the London Artists' Association, which had sponsored them so far, and were taken on instead by Agnew's. Meanwhile, Julian was developing left-wing views. At Charleston, Vanessa's unique way of life was particularly appreciated by Roger Fry, even though he and Vanessa were no longer lovers. Sadly Roger died suddenly in 1934 after an accident to his hip: Vanessa was heartbroken. Virginia described him as 'the most lovable of all our friends'.[11]

Vanessa now took Angelica (aged 16) away from school at Easter, without her taking her school certificate, so as to arrive in Italy before the hot weather. Meanwhile Julian was appointed Professor of English at the National University of Wuhan at Hankow for three years. He and Vanessa kept up a close relationship through frequent letter-writing. Her daughter Angelica only got to know the identity of her true father, Duncan, in the summer of 1938, though she had suspected it before.[12]

Vanessa continued to paint, particularly portraits, including one of Margot Asquith, who in spite of her position in London's social life was not in the least a snob, according to Vanessa. At this point Vanessa and other Bloomsbury artists joined the Artists' International Association, founded in 1933 with the slogan 'Unity of Artists for Peace, Democracy and Cultural Development', which also provided a banner for anti-fascism. Quentin became involved in anti-fascist rallies; Julian, still in China, was caught *in flagrante* with the Chinese wife of a colleague, and had to resign his post and travel home.

Julian now thought the Republicans in the war in Spain were justified, and wanted to fight with them, but the family persuaded him to sign up with Spanish Medical Aid as an ambulance driver instead. Meanwhile Duncan, Clive and Vanessa visited Picasso's studio in Paris, where his work *Guernica* was in progress. Julian set off for Spain, leaving behind several grieving women besides Vanessa. He joined the 35th Division Medical Service at El Escorial and then went to Villanueva de la Cañada, within sight of the front, with plenty of action. He was in his element. But it was not to last.

Julian volunteered as a stretcher-bearer: he was then in charge of a lorry to transport the wounded. His lung caught a bit of flying shrapnel, and though surgeons removed it, he died soon afterwards. On hearing the news Vanessa suffered a complete breakdown. Only Virginia could offer any kind of comfort, but Clive wrote in a letter: 'I doubt whether the hole in Vanessa's life will be filled up ever'.[13] John Maynard Keynes wrote an obituary for King's College Cambridge and a warm letter to Vanessa, who also received a letter from Julian himself, to be given to her if the worst happened.

Vanessa's grief was overwhelming, and she found it difficult to work. Slowly she recovered, comforted by Duncan, and indeed by painting, when she was able to return to it. There is perhaps no more agonizing blow than the death of a child, and Julian was also a particularly close companion. Once again she had to repress her emotions and live through a serious crisis. 'Her work became, particularly in later life, a refuge from these dark emotions…'[14] As regards work, the next development of the Bloomsbury group was the foundation of the 'Euston Road School' in 1938, heralded by Clive Bell as 'a critical movement for English painting'.[15] It took in part-time students and had something of a left-wing bias. Vanessa was also busy editing Julian's letters for publication.

Angelica was Vanessa's next preoccupation: it seemed that the relationship between her and Bunny (David Garnett), who was 26 years older than her, with a wife and two sons, was giving cause for concern. Vanessa wanted Angelica to be happy, and was not so wary of the relationship as was Duncan, who challenged Bunny about it. The next crisis was Angelica's severe cystitis, necessitating urgent treatment in a nursing home. As war approached, Charleston came into its own once more, and Vanessa made various alterations to the house. Painting continued, being the chief occupation not only of Vanessa but also of Duncan, Angelica and Quentin. But Vanessa continued to find Bunny's visits difficult, and there was still a barrier between herself and Angelica. Though her dress was informal, even sloppy, her emotions were tightly controlled.

War was declared on 3rd September 1939: Bunny was called up. Quentin had been rejected owing to tuberculosis, but now worked as a farm labourer for Maynard. Clive was on a British Council committee arranging for British art to be sent abroad. Vanessa kept chickens and Walter Higgins, the gardener, grew vegetables. Angelica celebrated her 21st birthday, and in May 1940 went with Bunny to his Yorkshire cottage: by now his wife had died (of breast cancer), and the affair was no longer a secret.

During the war Clive and Quentin joined the Home Guard, and Walter Higgins, the gardener, now went to work elsewhere, so Clive, Vanessa and Duncan took care of the garden. Some of the Bloomsbury properties were bombed, and many paintings damaged. Virginia was again subject to serious mental illness: she was hearing voices and felt suicidal. She finally drowned herself in the nearby river Ouse: once more Vanessa was struck down physically with grief, and was also concerned for Leonard. Her brother Adrian was now a leading psychoanalyst, but Vanessa herself was inclined to bottle up her feelings, and sought no talking therapy. She now had two close family members to mourn, but it seems she was disinclined to speak about it. We may surmise that her immune system bore the brunt.

Her next task was to decorate nearby Berwick church, together with Duncan, Quentin and Angelica. She was constantly struggling, though, for time and space in which to work: 'We females have to struggle for it all our lives one way or another,' she wrote to Angelica.[16] Her biographer thinks that Vanessa 'used the religious subjects as an impersonal cloak for her own feelings and experience':[17] her experience of her son's death mirrored that of the Virgin Mary. Her next emotional upheaval was over the marriage of Angelica to Bunny. Vanessa and Duncan, her parents, were not invited to the wedding. In the spring of 1943 Angelica became pregnant, and she and Bunny made a reconciliatory visit to Charleston. The child (Amaryllis Virginia) was born before Christmas, when there were joyful celebrations at Charleston. With the advent of flying bombs life in London was increasingly hazardous, and excursions to the city were avoided if at all possible.

In August 1944 at the age of 65 Vanessa found a lump in her breast: she told no one except Quentin, but arranged to have a mastectomy in a Hove nursing home. That Christmas, celebrations were enlivened by presents brought back from America by Maynard and Lydia. But beneath the festivities lay Vanessa's suffering. Kenneth Clark observed that her integrity was unblemished.

> She was not at all dogmatic, but she never relaxed her standards, and in a quiet, hesitant voice would expose false values and mixed motives. I was devoted to her, and when asked to do something questionable, I would think to myself 'What would Vanessa say?'[18]

She also displayed a reserve, which increased with the years. But she continued painting, as well as being absorbed in her grandchildren. Angelica had a second daughter soon after Victory in Europe (VE) Day (8th May 1945), and twin girls in December 1946. John Maynard Keynes had been increasingly suffering from heart problems, and died suddenly on Easter Sunday 1946. His widow Lydia was now more warmly received at Charleston.

After the war Vanessa and Duncan were keen to go abroad, and made various excursions to Dieppe, Paris, and Venice. But Vanessa's grief over Julian's death was unabated, expressed according to Angelica as 'drab, unstylish clothes, a shrinking from society and the constant reiteration that Duncan's work was so infinitely better than her own'.[19] But Duncan himself had 'the very highest opinion possible to have' of her as an artist, as he wrote to her in December 1948.[20] Vanessa continued to have left-wing political views, and voted Labour in 1950. She was also agnostic, and would turn off the radio when the religious service came on: this in opposition to her grandchildren, who sang hymns in the house. Another grandchild arrived, named Julian, soon after Quentin married Anne Olivier Popham, and then another, Virginia. Vanessa was delighted with her grandchildren.

Charleston was a convenient place to visit for those on their way to Glyndebourne, the country opera house, and guests were frequent. There were more trips abroad, to France, and Venice. Back home in Charleston life continued in a regular, disciplined fashion: Vanessa even restricted her smoking to three cigarettes a day. (At the time, people did not realize how harmful smoking was, and this would have seemed very little.)

In February 1956 Vanessa held a successful exhibition in the Adam Gallery in London. Her creative fire continued. In 1956 Duncan designed sets for the opera *Venus and Adonis* by John Blow, performed at Aldeburgh, which led to a meeting with Benjamin Britten and Peter Pears, and their return visit to Charleston. However, Vanessa's health was failing, with pleurisy in early 1959. A holiday in January 1960 in La Source in northern Italy near Menton was beneficial. To quote her biographer, Vanessa had 'found in painting the philosopher's stone to transmute suffering into serenity'.[23] In April 1961 Vanessa fell ill again, this time with bronchitis. She died on 7th April, watched over by Quentin. She was buried in Firle churchyard, without any ceremony, and a plain black tombstone was erected.

Vanessa was nearly 82 when she died — a respectable age for anyone. She had survived cancer for nearly 17 years. I suggest that her cancer may well have been related to her overwhelming grief over the deaths of her son and her sister, on top of several earlier bereavements including the loss of her brother Thoby, and abuse from her half-brother, leading to a coping mechanism where she bottled up her feelings and did not talk about them. In the case of Virginia, early abuse may well have been the trigger for serious mental illness, finally ending in suicide. However, Vanessa found meaning in her work, her creative fire was not foiled, and her cancer did not recur: she died of a complaint common among the elderly. Perhaps it was her art that served as life-affirming therapy, as well as her delight in her grandchildren. She was at the very centre of a remarkable movement, the Bloomsbury group, and she will be long remembered.

Select Bibliography

Quentin Bell and Virginia Nicholson:
Charleston: a Bloomsbury house and garden (Frances Lincoln Ltd, London, 1997). This book, beautifully produced, contains many colour photographs, including those of Vanessa's work, as well as reminiscences by her son Quentin.

Vanessa Bell:
Sketches in Pen and Ink, ed. Lia Giachero (Pimlico, London, 1998)

Jane Dunn:
Virginia Woolf and Vanessa Bell: a very close conspiracy (Jonathan Cape, London, 1990; paperback edition Virago, London, 2000)

Angelica Garnett:
Deceived with Kindness: a Bloomsbury childhood (Pimlico, London, 1995). Angelica herself underwent a mastectomy, and says in her Epilogue: 'I am convinced it was a result more of my unhealthy state of mind than of my body.' (p. 175)

Judy Moore:
The Bloomsbury Trail in Sussex (S.B. Publications, Seaford, 1995)

Jans Ondaatje Rolls:
The Bloomsbury Cookbook: recipes for Life, Love and Art (Thames and Hudson, London, 2014). This contains many colour reproductions of Vanessa's paintings, a lengthy bibliography and helpful 'chronology of Bloomsbury'.

Frances Spalding:
Vanessa Bell (Weidenfeld & Nicolson, London, 1983; paperback edition Phoenix Giants, London, 1996)

Notes

1.   Spalding, p. 18.
2.   V. Bell, p. 99.
3.   G.E. Moore, *Principia Ethica,* 1903, p. 189, quoted in Spalding, p. 65.
4.   Spalding, p. 92.
5.   *ibid.,* p. 92.
6.   *ibid.,* p. 164.
7.   Bell and Nicholson, p. 20.
8.   Rolls, p. 75.
9.   R. Fry to H. Anrep, 15th August 1926, quoted in Spalding, p. 210.
10. Spalding, p. 237.
11. *ibid.,* p. 267.
12. Garnett, p. 246.
13. Spalding, p. 298.
14. Dunn, p. 240.
15. Spalding, p. 302.
16. *ibid.,* p. 320.
17. *ibid.,* p. 320.
18. *ibid.,* p. 326.
19. *ibid.,* p. 337.
20. *ibid.,* p. 361.

Rachel Carson

AT A TIME WHEN ENVIRONMENTALISTS are becoming increasingly concerned about the misuse of pesticides and the plastic pollution of the oceans, the story of Rachel Carson, author of *Silent Spring*, is of particular interest. She was born on 27th May 1907, in Springdale, Pennsylvania, the daughter of Marie and Robert Carson, who came from Irish stock. Her father was a farmer, not very successful, and a self-employed travelling insurance salesman. Rachel had an older brother and sister, but was fairly solitary: her companions were wild creatures. She also liked to draw, and was a great reader, particularly of Beatrix Potter stories. At about the age of eight she started writing herself, and later contributed prize-winning stories to the *St Nicholas* children's magazine.

She attended high school for her last year at Parnassus, two miles away. She was then admitted to the Pennsylvania College for Women (PCW), a private college, with a scholarship of $100; her parents still had to pay $800 for her room and board. Her mother made considerable sacrifices to find the money, and perhaps for this reason, Rachel always deferred to her in later life. She made excellent academic progress, but her social development was cramped by the constant weekend visits of her mother. Her natural reserve added to her social isolation.

She registered for a wide syllabus of classes in the arts, and in her first essay on 'Who I am and why I came to PCW' she wrote of her real love: 'I love all the beautiful things of nature, and the wild creatures are my friends.'[1] In her first year she gained good grades, especially for her essays on nature subjects. But her summer vacation was difficult, with her brother Robert and his wife and baby daughter Frances creating problems at home. Rachel and her mother were called upon to babysit: not just Frances but also two other nieces, daughters of her sister Marian, who had returned home because her marriage had broken up.

Returning to college, Rachel added psychology to her course in biology, English, and French. She was taught biology by Professor Mary Scott Skinker, who was acting head of the biology department. She was much impressed by Rachel's ability and high standards. In turn, Rachel was impressed by Professor Skinker's brilliance. So in spite of the traditional chasm between literature and science, Rachel began to build her own bridge from one to the other. This resulted in a compelling literary style, unusual among scientists, which gave added impetus to her scientific writing, and for which she would become famous.

During the summer of 1929 Rachel joined a group of scientists and teachers at Woods Hole, near Boston, where the Marine Biological Laboratory (MBL) had its headquarters, and spent six weeks there. Here women were welcomed, and the atmosphere was relaxed. Live specimens of marine life were available for study. Rachel wrote to a friend: 'The town is much more attractive than I'd expected to find it. One can't walk very far in any direction without running into water.'[2] There was also a good research library, with extensive information about the sea. Her opportunities for research unfolded, and she pursued her interest in reptiles, working towards her master's thesis.

Back in Washington at Johns Hopkins University, Rachel did well in her first year at graduate school. But the Depression was a difficult time for students, and Rachel's parents could not help her. She fell behind in her research, when her squirrel specimens ran into breeding difficulties, which delayed her degree. But she was highly recommended for an assistantship at the Dental and Pharmacy School of the University of Maryland in College Park, Maryland. She was appointed the only female biology teacher in the Dental School. She also started a research project on the urinary system of fish. But she had to request a year's delay to finish the project, which ran into difficulties with the supply of specimens. Finally it was finished in April 1932, and she was awarded her master's degree.

However, Rachel was still in debt for her undergraduate studies, and asked PCW to release her from the debt: they eventually agreed, in return for assigning mortgaged land to them. The Depression tightened, and Rachel's father was in increasingly poor health. She was obliged to relinquish her doctoral candidacy at Johns Hopkins University, and try for a teaching post. Although she had brilliant credentials, jobs were difficult to come by. Rachel turned to writing to earn money. Then her father died suddenly. Rachel's next job was to write radio scripts for the Bureau of Fisheries in Washington. She was ideally qualified, having both knowledge of marine life and a compelling writing style. She also wrote articles on the sea for local newspapers. She was concerned about the welfare of the fish as much as that of the fishermen.

In July 1936 she was appointed a junior aquatic biologist with the Division of Scientific Inquiry in the Bureau of Fisheries, which made her a full-time government scientist, one of only two women employed in such a post. This involved laboratory study and library research, and both her literary skills and her knowledge of marine life came into their own. She published articles on oyster farming, the shad, and commercial fishing in general. She visited Chesapeake

Bay and talked to local fishermen. She wrote about birds as well as fish, and her writing produced a modest income.

But another family tragedy struck: the death of her sister Marian from pneumonia, aged only 40, leaving two daughters, Virginia and Marjorie. Rachel's mother (aged nearly 70) accepted the responsibility of housekeeping and caring for the children, while Rachel (aged nearly 30) was the breadwinner. Commuting to her office in Baltimore was expensive, so she found a house for the family to rent in Silver Spring, Maryland, much nearer to her office, with good schools for the children nearby.

Rachel offered her essay 'The World of Water' to the *Atlantic Monthly*: the editor responded with enthusiasm. After several revisions it was published as 'Undersea', with a biographical note, for $100. It appeared in September 1937, and was a turning point for Rachel. Up till now she had not disclosed her gender, signing her articles 'R.C. Carson'. For the first time she now admitted to being a woman writer.

This brief essay caught the interest and enthusiasm of Quincy Howe, senior editor of Simon & Schuster, who suggested that she write a book on the subject of the sea. Hendrik Villem Van Loon, a Simon & Schuster author and illustrator, was similarly impressed. Van Loon invited Rachel to visit him and discuss the project. She responded swiftly with an outline of the book, which became *Under the Sea-Wind*. She aimed to describe the sea from the point of view of the sea creatures, not from that of man. But writing the book had to take second place to more lucrative short-term writing of reviews and articles for newspapers.

In summer 1938 she spent ten days with her family on holiday in a cottage on the east coast at Beaufort. Here she did research for *Under the Sea-Wind*, exploring the coast and observing wild life at night as well as during the day. She became increasingly interested in environmental health issues. Back in the Bureau of Fisheries, she was promoted to a new post in the field laboratory in College Park, Maryland. This involved writing many scientific reports and reviews of research. But finally she managed to finish her book, which was published in November 1941. In it she combined a serious scientific account of sea creatures and seasons with a poetic fluency that characterized all her writing. She describes birds around the shore as well as fish.

> *The heron stood motionless, his neck curved back on his shoulders, his bill poised to spear fish as they darted past his legs. As the terrapin moved out into deeper water she startled a young mullet and sent it racing towards the beach in confusion and panic. The sharp-eyed heron saw the movement and with a quick dart seized the fish crosswise in his bill. He tossed it into the air, caught it head first, and swallowed it. It was the first fish other than small fry that he had caught that night.[3]*

The book gained brilliant reviews. But the Japanese assault on Pearl Harbor and the entry of the USA into the Second World War diverted public attention elsewhere. The book sold only 2,000 copies, but Rachel formed a friendship with her editor, Maria Leiper. In April 1943 a new job opportunity arose for a position as 'associate aquatic biologist' in the Office of the Coordinator of Fisheries in Washington. She and her mother moved back to Maryland.

At 36 Rachel was a successful civil servant as well as a popular science writer, with many friends and acquaintances. Because of the war, she was now asked to write public information bulletins on food from the sea, at a time when meat was rationed. She was promoted again, to 'aquatic biologist', and then to 'information specialist', in charge of information about the wartime fishery programme. Her workload increased, but her health deteriorated, with a succession of minor infections. She concentrated now on magazine articles rather than books. Though she now had a good job, her responsibilities to her family were increasing.

Rachel still needed the salary from her civil service job, but she longed to give it up and be a freelance writer. A new and compelling topic had arisen: the use of pesticides and their effect on fish and other wildlife. The insecticide DDT was of particular concern, and reports on DDT came to her for editing. She offered to write on the subject for the *Reader's Digest*, but was turned down, so DDT was put back in her bottom drawer, to emerge later in her most famous book, *Silent Spring*. Meanwhile DDT was released for civilian use without proper testing.

Rachel's private life was now not as stressed as before: her nieces Marjorie and Virginia had left school and had jobs, and her mother continued to keep house. Rachel drove to work and met friends at weekends. But finding time for writing was still a problem. Her outings with friends included expeditions to bird refuges, in particular the Hawk Mountain Sanctuary in eastern Pennsylvania. Through an article she wrote, 'Bird Banding is their Hobby', she became friends with the much older Ada Govan of the Woodland Bird Sanctuary in Lexington, Massachusetts, a relationship conducted almost entirely by letter (Ada was more or less housebound after a fall), but intense all the same. Both of them loved Henry Williamson's writing (especially *Salar the Salmon*). A letter to Ada from Rachel confessed:

> No, my life isn't at all well ordered and I don't know where I'm going. I know that if I could choose what seems to me the ideal existence, it would be just to live by writing. But I have done far too little to dare risk it. And all the while my job with the Service grows and demands more and more of me, leaving less time that I could put on my own writing. And as my salary increases little by little, it becomes even more impossible to give it up! That is my problem right now, and not knowing what to do about it, I do nothing.[4]

Although Rachel's career as a civil servant was progressing well, it was still preventing her from getting on with her writing. She described her job as follows:

> My job consists of the general direction of the publishing program of the Fish and Wildlife's information service — working with authors in planning and writing their

manuscripts, reviewing manuscripts submitted, and overseeing the actual editing and preparation of the manuscript for the printer. I have a staff of six...[5]

However, her 'Conservation in Action' series of booklets went some way towards her general aim of educating the public on the subject of the preservation of wildlife. She wrote: 'Wildlife, water, forests, grasslands, all are part of man's essential environment: the conservation and effective use of one is impossible except as the others also are conserved.'[6] Research for these booklets took time, and on-site study, such as an expedition to the waterfowl refuge on Assateague Island, Virginia.

In June 1946 Rachel took a month's leave to visit the coast of Maine with her mother, staying in a cottage near the water's edge. She was enchanted by the birds as well as the sea creatures, and the pine forests, and wrote about them compellingly. This was a place she fell in love with; she would gladly have spent the rest of her life there had it been financially feasible. In fact she did then win $1,000, the second prize in an essay competition for *Outdoor Life* magazine, on the subject of the reasons for conserving natural resources.

Her day job now took her on trips researching for the 'Conservation in Action' booklets. One of these trips took her as far as the Pacific Ocean for the first time, together with Katherine (Kay) Howe, an artist and photographer who supplied the necessary visual material. The resulting publications were hugely successful, drawing the attention of the public to the importance of the conservation of natural environments and resources.

Rachel worked on this project for two and a half years: it both enriched her knowledge of ecology and gave her great happiness. However, there was a cost to her very fully extended efforts to combine a demanding day job with her private writing and her role as aunt, sister, and daughter. Between 1945 and 1947 she underwent three hospital visits, for the removal of her appendix, a breast cyst (which was benign), and haemorrhoids. But Rachel was not one to complain. Further stress was always there in the form of constant deadlines, and office politics. Her mother too had surgery, during which Rachel had to care for her, and manage the household. In January 1948 she developed shingles, for which stress is recognized to be a risk factor. This set her writing back yet again.

In August 1948 Rachel engaged a new wildlife illustrator, Bob Hines, very experienced, from the Ohio Division of Conservation. He became a good friend. Rachel was then promoted to the job of Chief Editor of the Bureau of Fisheries. Evenings and weekends were spent on research for her new book. After the mediocre success of *Under the Sea-Wind* with Simon & Schuster, Rachel wanted to find another publisher, and a new friend, Charles Allridge, suggested using a literary agent: finally Marie Rodell was engaged to take on the task of finding a publisher for Rachel's new book, provisionally titled *Return to the Sea*.

Around the same time came the news that Rachel's old friend Mary Scott Skinker was dying of cancer. Rachel borrowed the money for the flight to Chicago to visit her. She died soon afterwards, and Rachel, in her own words, was 'pretty well shot to pieces'.[6] Mary Scott Skinker was Rachel's mentor and intimate friend, and had given emotional support for her life's work. However, she was soon to find a new friend in Marie Rodell, her literary agent.

Marie was a graduate of Vassar, with editorial experience in three different publishing firms, and a member of MENSA (the high-IQ society). In 1948 she struck out on her own as a literary agent. Younger than Rachel, and briefly married to John Rodell, she was the ideal agent for Rachel, sharing her uncompromising ideals and efficient way of working: they collaborated well. Marie devised a clever programme of sales to magazines of chapters as they were written, to maximize their monetary value. Slowly the script of what became *The Sea Around Us* was written, and Marie and Rachel were on first-name terms (Marie called her 'Ray'). On 6th September 1948 Rachel wrote to her: 'These relationships [i.e. man's with the ocean], and my belief that we will become even more dependent upon the ocean as we destroy the land, are really the theme of the book...'[7] The present plastic pollution of the sea would have horrified her.

Philip Vaudrin, the editor of Oxford University Press (in America), agreed to publish *The Sea Around Us* on the basis of an outline and specimen chapter Rachel had given to Marie. A research trip was now planned to the Georges Bank, east of Boston: Marie went along as a 'chaperone' to Rachel, in the company of an otherwise all male crew.

Another trip was to the interior of the Everglades refuge, with Shirley Briggs, an expedition never before undertaken by women. Rachel was less successful in her attempts at diving, which she only achieved once, but valued hugely, regarding it as a milestone in her experience of the sea. Her next trip was with Marie Rodell, on the *Albatross III*, which was working to conserve the fish of the New England banks. Rachel's job was to research the role of the ship, for publication in her series of booklets. She observed the catch coming in, and found the deep-water starfish 'especially lovely, and sometimes there were heart urchins and such odd beings as sea mice. Scores of different species of fishes were brought up to give their own mute testimony as to who lived down in the undersea world of Georges Bank.'[8]

The voyage had cemented the relationship between Rachel and Marie, and their letters now ended 'with love'. They needed to be on excellent terms during the coming months, when Rachel struggled to meet the deadline for completion of *The Sea Around Us*, which was finally published by Oxford University Press, with nine of its fourteen chapters serialized in the *New Yorker*, condensed by its editor William Shawm. However, OUP in England declined publication, and it was offered instead to Staples Press in London, who published the British edition.

The waiting had been stressful, and Rachel discovered another lump in her left breast in September 1950. It was removed, and pronounced non-malignant, and again Rachel seemed to react with equanimity: characteristically she didn't make a fuss, and continued her seashore research. There was also more good news to keep her going. Her essay 'The Birth of an Island' was honoured with an award of $1,000. She was also awarded a Guggenheim Fellowship in March 1951, which enabled her to take a year's leave of absence from her civil service job. Even better, *The Sea Around Us* was chosen for the Book of the Month Club as an 'alternate'. Requests poured in for media interviews. The serialization in the *New Yorker* was a huge success, giving rise to an unprecedented volume of correspondence.

The book was launched at a successful party. Rachel's combination of literary gifts and scientific knowledge was lavishly praised. *The Sea Around Us* was a top bestseller for 86 weeks, and received excellent reviews. Fan mail poured in (this was acknowledged by her mother) and OUP had to order several reprints: the book was soon out of stock.

Media interest was high, centring to some extent on the fact that she was a woman. (Some reviewers even speculated that 'she' must be a man.) Cyrus Dingin of the *Boston Globe* reported: 'She is small and slender... trim and feminine, wears a soft pink nail polish and uses lipstick and powder expertly, but sparingly.'[9] Would such physical details have been noted if she had been a man? That such a person could also be an accomplished scientist was obviously a surprise.

At this point Rachel managed to assign the rights for her first book, *Under the Sea-Wind,* to join *The Sea Around Us,* which had been a bestseller for months, with Oxford University Press. She accepted speaking engagements, and at a lunch in Washington spoke about her correspondence:

> *It has come to me very clearly through these wonderful letters that people everywhere are desperately eager for whatever will lift them out of themselves and allow them to believe in the future. I am sure that such release from tension can come through the contemplation of the beauties and mysterious rhythms of the natural world.[10]*

So began her crusade for environmentalism. But she was herself in need of spiritual solace. She returned home to find that her niece Marjorie was pregnant by a married man. The pregnancy was too advanced to contemplate an abortion, so Rachel and her mother made the necessary arrangements to care for Marjorie; at a time when she should have been enjoying her literary success Rachel was enduring a private tragedy.

At her next public appearance, on 16th October 1951, Rachel herself tackled the subject of being a woman scientist:

> *People often seem to be surprised that a woman has written a book about the sea. This is especially true, I find, of men. Perhaps they have been accustomed to thinking of the more exciting fields of scientific knowledge as exclusively masculine domains. Then even if they accept my sex, some people are further surprised to find that I am not a tall, oversize, Amazon-type female.[11]*

She became an expert public speaker, working on her speeches with her usual care and thoroughness. Meanwhile *The Sea Around Us* was doing well, and was translated into 32 languages, and even turned into a film script. In January 1952 Rachel won the National Book Award for non-fiction, and was invited to New York to make a speech. The citation ran:

> *Rachel L. Carson's* The Sea Around Us *brings to the attention of the public a hitherto unconsidered field of scientific inquiry of great importance to the spiritual and material economy of mankind. It is a work of scientific accuracy presented with poetic imagination and such clarity of style and originality of approach [as] to win and hold every reader's attention.*[12]

Rachel's speech focused on her mission to draw together science and literature in a manner understandable by the general reader:

> *Many people have commented with surprise on the fact that a work of science should have a large popular sale. But this notion that 'science' is something that belongs in a separate compartment of its own, apart from everyday life, is one that I should like to challenge. We live in a scientific age; yet we assume that knowledge of science is the prerogative of only a small number of human beings, isolated and priestlike in their laboratories. This is not true. It cannot be true. The materials of science are the materials of life itself. Science is part of the reality of living; it is the what, the how, and the why of everything in our experience. It is impossible to understand man without understanding his environment and the forces that have molded him physically and mentally.*[13]

Even more prestigious than the National Book Award, Rachel also gained the Burroughs Medal for *The Sea Around Us*. In her acceptance speech she stressed the importance of the public understanding of science, at a time when fears of nuclear warfare were escalating. 'Mankind… seems to be going farther and farther into more experiments for the destruction of himself and his world.'[14]

Further honours awaited her: the *New York Times* voted *The Sea Around Us* the outstanding book of 1951, and 250,000 copies of the book were sold by the end of the year. She was also awarded the Henry Grier Bryant Gold Medal for distinguished services to geography, and another Gold Medal from the New York Zoological Society. More public speaking followed, and an honorary doctorate of letters from the Drexel Institute of Technology. Her old college, the PCW, awarded her an honorary doctorate. However, all these public appearances and requests for speeches were tiring her out.

Under the Sea-Wind now did extremely well on the OUP list, in contrast to its lukewarm reception first time round. Even the UK honoured Rachel: she was elected to a fellowship of the Royal Society of Literature. Back home she was criticized by some who considered she ignored God as creator, but Rachel gave them an elegant answer:

> *Believing as I do in evolution, I merely believe that is the method by which God created and is still creating life on earth. And it is a method so marvelously conceived that to study it in detail is to increase — and certainly never to diminish — one's reverence and awe both for the Creator and the process.*[15]

Rachel was now financially independent, but still employed by the Fish and Wildlife Service. She launched on yet another book, to become *The Edge of the Sea*. For some time now Rachel had wanted to resign from her civil service job in order to concentrate on her writing, and she finally managed this on 3rd June 1952. She and her mother set off for Massachusetts and the Marine Biological Laboratory, where she researched in the library. She also bought some land near the sea where she planned to build a small house.

A review by Henry Beston of *Under the Sea-Wind* summed up her talent perfectly. 'It is Miss Carson's particular gift to be able to blend scientific knowledge with the spirit of poetic awareness, thus restoring to us a true sense of the world.'[16] Then came a disappointment: the dispute with Irwin Allen, who was turning *The Sea Around Us* into a film. She found his script embarrassingly amateur, and also inaccurate. She could not stop the film being made, but vowed never to sell film rights to her work again.

Rachel was very happy in her new cottage in Maine, and even better, she made friends with some interesting summer holiday neighbours, Dorothy and Stanley Freeman. She formed a particularly warm friendship with Dorothy, who was nine years her senior. She had had to resign her job teaching home economics when she married Stanley Freeman—as women had to do at the time. For Rachel she filled an emotional gap. Her mother Maria was becoming increasingly dependent on her, and she needed a break. Rachel and Dorothy wrote many letters to each other, exchanging poems and books, and finally calling each other 'Dearest' and 'Darling'. Rachel told Dorothy that she loved her. The relationship became passionate. Their more personal letters often enclosed second letters that could be read aloud to the family. Dorothy understood Rachel's creativity, and also her intellectual side.

Rachel sent her a first edition of *The Sea Around Us*, with the note:

> *...When I finally became its biographer, the sea brought me recognition and what the world calls success.*
>
> *It brought me to Southport.*
>
> *It brought me to you.*
>
> *So now the sea means something to me that it never meant before. And even the title of the book has a new and personal significance—the sea around Us.*[17]

Her new book, *The Edge of the Sea*, based on her own fieldwork, was again full of poetic descriptions of sea creatures and literary allusions:

> *It is a fantastic jungle, mad in a Lewis Carroll sort of way. For what proper jungle, twice every twenty-four hours, begins to sag lower and lower and finally lies prostrate for several hours, only to rise again? Yet this is precisely what rockweed jungles do.*[18]

Another significant piece of writing was 'Help your child to wonder', a contribution to *Woman's Home Companion*, which might have been (but wasn't) expanded into a book. But a new idea took precedence: the work on pesticides that finally became *Silent Spring*. However, her time was severely restricted as she had to care increasingly for her mother, aged 88, whose health was deteriorating. Her niece Marjorie also became seriously ill, and soon after died at the age of only 31, leaving her son Roger to be cared for by Rachel. At the age of nearly 50, Rachel became *in loco parentis* to Roger, aged only five. The physical and emotional strain on her must have been immense, and since she had to care for Roger she could not allow herself time to grieve for Marjie. Roger was a demanding child, and Rachel felt anxious and alone, even desperate, with her problems.

At the same time a new interest arose. New chemicals (chlordane, dieldrin, aldrin, DDT) had been developed during the Second World War, and the U.S. Department of Agriculture proposed aerial spraying of farmland so as to eradicate the fire ant, introduced from Brazil during the war. Congressional hearings on the proposal were held, and it was opposed by wildlife advocates, who were concerned about the threat to beneficial insects as well as to birds. Although Roger was now at school, his health too was not great, and he demanded considerable attention. But the new book had to be written. Rachel had been concerned about the irresponsible use of pesticides for some time, and now the topic was once again in the news.

In 1957 residents of Long Island sought to halt the aerial spraying of private land with DDT. Rachel wanted to warn the public about the dangers of pesticide abuse, which might threaten human as well as animal health, and her final and most important book began to take shape, and was commissioned by Houghton Mifflin. Rachel was in touch with many other campaigners, such as Olga Huckins, who with her husband owned a property where many song-birds had died as a result of repeated aerial spraying of mosquitoes. Moreover, the surviving mosquitoes were even stronger and more pernicious than before.

But DDT was not only harmful to insects: it was rated a chemical carcinogen by Wilhelm Hueper, at the National Cancer Institute. The evidence for this was substantial, and it formed the material for two chapters of Rachel's book, which carefully explained the way in which carcinogenic chemicals could be stored in the body for years before producing tumours or leukaemia. She regarded this as her most important message. The same controversy rages today over glyphosate, classed as a probable carcinogen by the World Health Organization and the IARC (International Agency for Research on Cancer) but widely used in parks and gardens all over the UK.

Rachel wrote to Dorothy: 'I feel, darling, that this may well outweigh in importance everything else I have done.'[19] Rachel was working very hard, staying up late and rising early, trying to finish her book, but she was cheered in December 1959 by the 'Lifetime Achievement Award' from the American Association of University Women, which included a stipend of $2,500. However, her tendency to overwork had a price: she developed a duodenal ulcer, followed by viral pneumonia and a sinus infection. She became depressed. But she carried on working.

Meanwhile her body encountered an even worse challenge. She found two new lumps in her left breast, and was told that one was 'bordering on malignant', so agreed to a mastectomy. She was concerned mainly about the effect of her hospitalization on Roger, now eight, who tended to get into trouble at school. Rachel was determined to keep the details of her illness private, but her friends were suspicious about her pathology reports, and felt she should have had further treatment. Her recovery from what sounds like brutal surgery was slow: and of course her work schedule was wrecked.

Later she found out that her doctors had not told her the truth even though she had asked for it: the cancer had already metastasized, and several underarm lymph nodes had been affected. It seems that her physicians deliberately withheld the truth from her since her prognosis was poor. However, she did make some progress on her book, working part of the time propped up in bed and dictating to her assistant Jeanne Davis. She also had a research assistant, Bette Harry.

Apart from the noxious effect of pesticides she was also concerned about radioactive contamination of the planet, 'for once radioactive elements have been deposited at sea they are irretrievable. The mistakes that are made now are made for all time.'[19] At the time there were particular public concerns about nuclear fallout. There were parallels between radiation hazards and those of chemical pesticides. During the autumn of 1960, while fighting cancer and struggling to finish her book, she even found time to work for the election of John F. Kennedy as president of the USA: she hoped that a Democratic administration would give higher priority to the problems of pollution.

Rachel's work on her book was interrupted by another hospital visit: she found a new lump in her left rib in November 1960. Her doctors decided on radiotherapy, but after only two treatments it made her feel very ill. She also lost faith in her doctors, and asked to change to George Crile at the Cleveland Clinic. His reading of her notes revealed that her previous doctors had certainly misled her. When she managed to visit Cleveland she was told the truth by Crile: that she had cancer that had metastasized to underarm lymph nodes. He recommended, first, sterilization by irradiating her ovaries (Rachel was still menstruating). Crile referred her to a radiologist at the Washington Hospital Center, and in January 1961 she started another series of ten radiotherapy treatments.

Of course all this set her writing back yet again. She was also aware of what little time she probably had left, and talked of death with Dorothy. She suffered severely with the radiotherapy, which was accompanied by various ailments: a bladder infection, then phlebitis in both legs. She spent six days in hospital, but even after returning home still had to visit hospital daily for her radiotherapy. Philosophically, Rachel regarded her long spell away from work as an opportunity to gain perspective. After a summer break in Southport, taking Roger with her, she returned home for her final spurt of creativity on the book. In January 1962 she sent 15 chapters of her book to Marie Rodell, her agent. The end was in sight, and also the public interest in the subject of pesticides was increasing. She wrote to William Shawm: 'I think the material is quite impressive...'[20]

Shawm agreed, phoning her back to congratulate her. Greatly encouraged, Rachel settled down to write the final chapter. Paul Brooks at Houghton Mifflin was similarly excited, writing to Rachel: 'I cannot imagine anyone else who possesses the combination of scientific understanding and literary skill to make such a fine book out of such difficult and complicated material.'[21] She set to work, also discussing publicity with Marie Rodell and the possibility of libel suits from chemical companies. This was a real anxiety, and Rachel did her very best to make sure that her text was scrupulously accurate, seeking critical comments from several experts in the field.

In the middle of all this, Rachel discovered more painful lumps in her right armpit. She went back to Cleveland for a consultation with Crile, who confirmed further metastases, for which he prescribed not further surgery but more radiation. She returned home and resumed radiotherapy, which made her nauseous. Of course she also worried about the long-term effects of such therapy. However, the good news was that the book was finished and proofs were expected soon. Publicity events were planned, and Rachel swore her friends to secrecy on the subject of her cancer, while also ordering a wig to conceal the damage to her hair. However, in spite of the radiotherapy the cancer was advancing: there was another painful node in her armpit.

Publication of *Silent Spring* was now planned for September, with serialization in three instalments in *The New Yorker* beginning on 16th June. Rachel attended the White House conference on conservation, where many of the delegates had received proof copies of *Silent Spring*. Triumph was to come: *Silent Spring* was to become the October Book of the Month. The *Audubon Magazine* also published excerpts, with the permission of *The New Yorker*, in which the first instalment aroused huge interest, but also provoked reaction from the business community, some of whom regarded Rachel as a 'Communist'.

On the publication of *Silent Spring* on 27th September 1962 the chemical companies were unsurprisingly up in arms: Velsicol threatened to sue, but Rachel remained calm, producing sources for all her statements in the book. In a press conference President Kennedy reported that the Department of Agriculture was looking at the long-range side effects from the use of pesticides.

Rachel was swamped with requests for interviews, and she had to shield Roger from her own publicity, which involved *CBS Reports* taking film footage of her in her cottage and surroundings. She also attended a launch cocktail party hosted by Houghton Mifflin, followed by several other public appearances at which she made speeches. She was also invited to a 'Kennedy seminar' at the White House, emphasizing there the futility of chemical pesticides. The Cuban Missile Crisis drew attention elsewhere, but attacks from the chemical industry continued, often from people who obviously had not even read the book. Meanwhile Rachel was coping with new pains in her back, needing further radiotherapy treatment, which caused more nausea. She even fainted while out shopping. Moreover, the onset of angina signalled another adverse effect from the radiotherapy. Again, her relationship with Dorothy kept her going.

As if her cancer was not enough to cope with, a vociferous campaign against *Silent Spring* was mounted by the chemicals industry, in particular the National Agricultural Chemicals Association (NACA), and the Monsanto Corporation, a leading pesticide manufacturer. Rachel was crudely attacked as a spinster with no children (why did that make her less of a scientist?). NACA labelled the book 'more poisonous than the pesticides she condemned'.[22] Most of her attackers were men, but one was a woman, Dr Cynthia Westcott, who had chaired the National Council of State Garden Clubs.

At the same time, Rachel had many of her own distinguished public defenders. She drew spiritual sustenance from unexpected letters of support from Thomas Merton, the theologian, and then even from Albert Schweitzer, a document that she had framed. Houghton Mifflin countered the negative press comments with another campaign, supported by several eminent scientists. New information came to her attention, which she used in public statements. In January 1963 she went to New York to receive the Schweitzer Medal from the Animal Welfare Institute, and to give a speech to the Garden Club of America. The following week she was in Boston to address the New England Wildflower Preservation Society, when Frank Egler, in the audience as Connecticut Chairman of the Wildflower Society, was impressed not only by her scientific soundness but also her feminine charm. But her angina pains became more frequent, and she had to decline many attractive invitations to speak from as far afield as Sweden.

Rachel wrote a tender letter to Dorothy, to be opened after her death. More painful lumps appeared in her neck, and bone metastases were diagnosed. She began more radiotherapy, accompanied by fatigue and nausea. She then embarked on a trial of the controversial drug Krebiozen, which did nothing to relieve her pelvic bone pain.

In April 1963 a television programme on the pesticide controversy was shown, the fruit of eight months' work, including interviews with Rachel and many eminent scientists, as well as representatives of the chemical industry. It drew an audience of ten to fifteen million, and was hugely influential. Rachel herself came over well. The President's Science Advisory Committee delivered a report, 'The Use of Pesticides', to the President, which largely supported Rachel's views. The report challenged not only the chemical industry but also government policy on pest control. Rachel was delighted. She then prepared to give evidence to two Senate committees. She advocated that spraying of pesticides should be brought under control. The senators were impressed by her integrity and her brilliance.

Rachel then set off for Southport for a summer break, and sent Roger to summer camp, leaving her to enjoy her time with Dorothy, though her health was declining fast, with bone metastases proving increasingly painful. Her cat Moppet died of pancreatitis, which made her very sad. Back in Silver Spring she underwent more investigations: she could now barely walk. She began a course of testosterone phosphorus to help with her bone pain. On the bright side was the news that the American Geographical Society proposed to award her the Cullum Medal. But criticism and attacks from the pesticide lobby continued.

In spite of her poor health she gave the opening lecture at the Kaiser Foundation symposium 'Man Against Himself' in San Francisco on 18th October: her title, 'The Pollution of the Environment', summed up her message. She sat to read her lecture, offering 'arthritis' as her excuse. She argued that modern pesticides were responsible for long-term contamination of the environment. Afterwards she visited Muir Woods and a Pacific Ocean beach with Marie Rodell and David Brown of the Sierra Club, in her wheelchair. By the time she got home she was in constant pain.

The assassination of President Kennedy on 22nd November 1963 was a further blow, since he had been helpful. Further alarming evidence of the dangers of pesticides arose from a huge fish kill in the Lower Mississippi River that same November. It was finally traced to endrin from a waste treatment plant owned by the Velsicol Corporation, who had tried to stop the publication of *Silent Spring*. More awards followed for Rachel, more prestigious appearances, which she struggled to attend, and more public debate about pesticides. She was now worried about who would continue her work after her death, but was reassured by a meeting with Margaret Owings, a supporter of various conservationist causes in California, assuring her that she would carry on the fight.

Rachel also had to think about her will, where to leave her papers, and making provision for Roger. This she did, but had great difficulty deciding on Roger's guardianship, in fact in the end leaving the decision to be made by her executors. She continued to work, though increasingly nauseous and in pain. The bone metastases were now beginning to affect her hand, making writing difficult. A night nurse moved in, luckily someone Roger liked. Rachel was now very anaemic from the radiation treatment, and was given blood transfusions. She now had liver metastases, but in spite of everything underwent yet more surgery in the form of a hypophesectomy (removal of the pituitary gland).

Thinking about the inevitable, she decided she wished to be cremated, and asked a clergyman from a Unitarian church, Duncan Howlett, to hold a memorial service for her when she died. He agreed. But to all but close friends she still pretended that her treatment was for arthritis. However, soon afterwards, on 14th April 1964, she suffered a heart attack and died.

Sadly, her brother Robert took no notice of her dying wish, and ordered a state funeral at the Washington National Cathedral, led by the Bishop of Washington. Duncan Howlett was forgotten. Robert stole some of Rachel's papers that he did not like, and even removed Roger's television set. In the end he had to agree to Rachel's wish to be cremated, burying half her ashes in Parklawn Cemetery alongside her mother, and the rest were scattered as she had wished at Southport. Paul and Susie Brooks became Roger's guardians. Marie Rodell did a scrupulous job of sorting out Rachel's papers, and on 25th June the inaugural meeting was held of what was to become the Rachel Carson Trust for the Living Environment. Her life's work was complete.

So why did Rachel suffer from breast cancer? 'Childless women get it' certainly. It seems that she was also subject to depression: she had plenty to be depressed about. Her childhood was somewhat lopsided, with a largely ineffective father and an omnipresent mother, who dominated her life and seems to have inhibited her social development, as well as requiring care herself until her death. She suffered bereavement of friends and family: the loss of Mary Scott Skinker hit her hard, and she had to care for several family members in difficult situations after further losses, without the support of a partner to share the burden.

Her intellectual and professional life was a struggle, initially for lack of finance, and later by prejudice against her gender. She also had to fight against the huge resources of the chemical industry in her *Silent Spring* campaign; but by then her cancer had made itself felt. How she managed to finish her book while in pain and (ironically) enduring more and more futile radiation treatments was something of a miracle: but her belief in the importance of her message and her spiritual strength somehow carried her through. We still need her inspiration today to save our planet from further destruction.

Select Bibliography

Note: the bibliographical history of Rachel Carson's books is somewhat confused. The date of the first American edition is given, followed by the edition now in print that I have consulted and have referred to in the text.

Rachel Carson: *Under the Sea-Wind* (Simon and Schuster, New York, 1941; Unicorn Press Ltd, London, 2014)

Rachel Carson: *The Sea Around Us* (Oxford University Press, New York, 1951; Unicorn Press Ltd, London, 2014)

Rachel Carson: *The Edge of the Sea* (Houghton Mifflin, Boston, 1955; Unicorn Press Ltd, London, 2015)

Rachel Carson: *Silent Spring* (Houghton Mifflin, Boston, 1962; Folio Society Edition, London, 2000)

Linda Lear: *Rachel Carson: Witness for Nature* (Henry Holt, USA, 1997; Penguin Books, London, 1998)

William Souder: *On a Farther Shore: the Life and Legacy of Rachel Carson* (Broadway Books, New York, 2012)

Notes

1. Lear, p. 30.
2. *ibid.*, p. 60.
3. Carson, *Under the Sea-Wind*, p. 14.
4. Carson, letter to Ada Govan, 15th February 1947, quoted in Lear, p. 130.
5. Carson, letter to Mrs W.S. Cole, 3rd November 1951, quoted in Lear, p. 131.
6. Carson, letter to Marie Rodell, 12th December 1948, quoted in Lear, p. 150.
7. Carson, letter to Marie Rodell, 26th March 1949, quoted in Lear, p. 161.
8. Carson, *The Real World Around Us*, quoted in Lear, p.171.
9. Quoted in Lear, p. 210.
10. Quoted in Lear, p. 210.
11. Quoted in Lear, p. 214.
12. Quoted in Lear, p. 218.
13. Quoted in Lear, pp. 218–19.
14. Quoted in Lear, p. 221.
15. Quoted in Lear, p. 227.
16. Quoted in Lear, p. 238.
17. Quoted in Souder, p. 197.
18. Carson, *The Edge of the Sea*, p. 73.
19. Quoted in Lear, p. 361.
20. Quoted in Lear, p. 373, from the preface to the revised edition of *The Sea Around Us* (OUP, New York, 1961).
21. Quoted in Lear, p. 396.
22. Quoted in Lear, p. 432.

Kathleen Ferrier

Kathleen was born on 22nd April 1912, the fourth child of Alice and William Ferrier, who lived in Higher Walton, a Lancashire village where her father was headmaster of the local primary school. Their first child had been stillborn, so the remaining three were warmly welcomed: Kathleen was the youngest. Winifred was eight years older, and George came in the middle. Both their parents were musical, and Kathleen too showed an early interest in the subject.

The family moved to Blackburn when her father obtained a better job with a higher salary. Kathleen learned quickly and could read before she went to school at age five. Her mother was ambitious for her and soon placed her in a fee-paying school, so had to go to work to cover the fees. She also arranged for Kathleen to have piano lessons, which enabled her to flourish musically: at the age of only 12 she came fourth out of 43 in a local music festival, and a year later she came second out of 26.

Her older brother George was however somewhat difficult, perhaps since he was extremely tall (6 ft 8 ins). Kathleen too was tall, and good at games as well as music, in fact something of a tomboy. All three children joined the Blackburn St Cecilia Vocal Union, taking part in *Messiah* and *Elijah*.

It was becoming obvious that Kathleen should go to music college, but instead she left school: her brother George was now in Canada, but was continually getting into scrapes. His parents felt they had to reserve any spare cash to get him out of trouble should the need arise: so to make sure the family could cope, Kathleen had to leave school and seek work (after all George was the only *boy*). So at the age of only 14, when she had already achieved Grade 8 in her piano exam for the Associated Board of the Royal Schools of Music, her mother overrode the headmistress's objections and found her a job in the local telephone exchange as a switchboard operator. She was soon put in charge of the telegram delivery boys — a rowdy bunch. In her spare time she played tennis, sang in a choir, and was also a Girl Guide.

She continued her piano studies with Miss Frances Walker. There then arose a great opportunity: a national musical competition for those under 17. Kathleen entered for her local area, and won. The prize was an upright Cramer piano. She now had to face the national finals in London, in which she was not successful, but all her expenses had been paid. Her teacher helped her to work towards the ARCM, and then the LRAM;* she now concentrated on her career as an accompanist, while still working at the telephone exchange.

'Kathleen was the best accompanist we ever had,' reported Ernest Allen, a tenor in the voice group 'The Sevilles'.[1] She was still working full time at the telephone exchange, and was not paid for these evening performances. However, she was professionally engaged as a soloist at a celebrity concert in Blackburn on 10 March 1929, and a year later in Blackburn again. In 1930 she won first prize and a Gold Medal at the Liverpool Festival, and also won the competition for under-19-year-olds at the Lytham St Anne's Festival. She was then asked to give a midday radio recital by BBC Manchester. She was not paid, and even lost money since she had to find someone to cover her office work. But it was a great achievement.

In May 1931 she passed her LRAM diploma, and then decided to start singing lessons with Anne Chadwick; after a few months she began to sing small parts in public. Her voice was a warm contralto, of exceptional quality. Even in these early days it was recognized as outstanding. Its full beauty can be appreciated in the many recordings that still exist: the one that is often played on BBC radio today is the unaccompanied folk song 'Blow the Wind Southerly'. She also took elocution lessons, since she wanted to make good speeches—something she was now called upon to do when receiving prizes.

Kathleen's next adventure was meeting Bert Wilson, a bank clerk with a Justice of the Peace for a father: he was a keen dancer and tennis player. They were attracted to one another; Bert was moved to another branch of the bank near Blackpool, and to be near him Kathleen transferred to the Blackpool Telephone Exchange, taking lodgings nearby, while Bert still lived at home with his parents in Chorley. Kathleen and Bert became engaged, to the delight of both sets of parents, though Kathleen's sister Winifred was not happy about it—as it turned out, with good reason.

Meanwhile Kathleen was gaining experience as a singer. She was also preparing for marriage to Bert, who had secured a company house at Lytham. Kathleen was beginning to have reservations about her future marriage, but didn't want to upset her family, and Bert's, who were so pleased about it. She felt trapped. Here perhaps was the first indication of the so-called 'cancer personality': the kind of person who bravely forges ahead, protesting 'I'm fine', while underneath they are suffering. But the wedding went ahead on 19th November 1935; she was already

---

*   ARCM: Associate of the Royal College of Music. LRAM: Licentiate of the Royal Academy of Music.

a local celebrity, and the event was reported in the *Blackburn Times*.

Kathleen now had to leave her job: married women could not be employed in the Post Office in those days. How would she now fill her time? And she did not love her husband: though she kept up appearances, the marriage was not consummated. This must have been a constant source of stress. However, Kathleen set about fulfilling her duty as a housewife, and to fill her days gave piano lessons, singing in the evenings with the Lytham Vocal Society, to which her husband also belonged. He was then promoted to Bank Manager, so they both had to move again to Silloth in Cumbria. Again she gave piano lessons, sang, joined local dramatic and musical societies, played golf and tennis, swam in the sea, and joined in the local social life. Her fighting spirit triumphed.

At the 1937 Carlisle Festival she came first in both the singing and the piano classes. She then really developed her singing. When she sewed on a button in a friend's house, a small boy called her 'Clever Kaff', and the nickname stuck—as 'Klever Kaff', which she adopted as her ironic signature to personal letters. Her career as a singer developed apace, but sadly her mother Alice did not live to rejoice in it: she died at only 66 of a strangulated hernia. Again Kathleen had a serious emotional setback.

In 1939 Kathleen once more competed in the Carlisle Festival, and won the trophy for the best solo singer. She was receiving more and more invitations to sing at concerts, and needed transport: her father William bought her a small car. He himself now moved to live with her sister Winifred in Edgware, London, where she had taken up a teaching post. Then the family agreed that he should not be left alone all day while Winifred was at work, and he came back to live with Kathleen and Bert. But their relationship was getting worse: Kathleen was achieving fame as a singer and leaving Bert behind. However, her father helped Kathleen with her music, and she started singing lessons with Dr J.E. Hutchinson in Carlisle, not far away. Her vocal technique improved and her repertoire widened.

Bert was conscripted into the army in 1940. This meant losing his company house, but the problem was solved by Winifred, who found a job teaching, with a house, in Carlisle, enabling Kathleen and her father to move in with her. Her next musical commitment was to CEMA, the Council for the Encouragement of Music and the Arts, a body that organized performers to visit offices, factories, and military camps during the war, to raise morale. This meant a good deal of travelling for Kathleen, and more caring for their father William for Winifred, but the family was pleased and proud, and Kathleen launched on a varied and successful career. She also teamed up with the soprano Isobel Baillie in performances of Handel's *Messiah*.

Kathleen was advised that she should move to London if she wanted to make a career in singing. The conductor Malcolm Sargent gave her an introduction to the concert agency Ibbs and Tillett. Eric Blom (the music critic) heard her rehearse for CEMA and was much impressed. But the summer of 1942 was blighted by bad weather for the 'holidays at home' concerts, and Kathleen had a hard time singing, particularly in Wednesbury in the open air, succumbing afterwards to a bad cold. The Mayor made amends by inviting her to give a concert in the Town Hall. Finally her audition with John Tillett in the Wigmore Hall took place, and was a success: Tillett welcomed her as a client. The move to London was now planned: Winifred managed to get a post in her old London school, and the three of them, Kathleen, Winifred and William, moved in on Christmas Eve 1942 to No. 2 Frognal Mansions, in Hampstead.

Kathleen was glad to be in London, not only to further her career but also to be within easy reach of good hospitals. She had occasional pains in her breast, apparently originating from early in her marriage, when Bert had accidentally caught it with his elbow. She believed that this could cause cancer, and every time she felt the pain, fear would seize her.

Her first London performance was at the National Gallery in a series of recitals organized by Dame Myra Hess. It was a success, but gave rise to the criticism that her performance lacked emotional depth. As Winifred remarked, Kathleen had been brought up in the north, where people tended to repress their feelings: Kathleen again showed the typical 'cancer personality', where feelings are kept under guard. She decided to ask the singer Roy Henderson for help, and he agreed to give her lessons, which started in March 1943. She kept on with her CEMA engagements, making many uncomfortable journeys in crowded and unheated wartime trains. Hotels too were far from congenial. But Kathleen was now earning her living as a singer, and overcame these difficulties. Her lessons with Henderson were going well, but her main asset was simply the quality of her voice, which captivated her audiences. The soprano Helen Anderson wrote:

> ...it was a real thrill to take part in concerts with her. It was partly voice and partly the warmth of her personality which communicated so strongly to her audiences. She so loved singing to people that they instinctively loved her back.[2]

In March 1943 she met Gerald Moore (a very distinguished accompanist), who played for her and gave her some useful tips about platform manner. After an excursion to Scotland, where she developed pneumonia and had to cancel several concerts, she was back in London for a performance of the *Messiah* with Isobel Baillie, Peter Pears (tenor) and William Parsons (bass), conducted by Reginald Jacques, in Westminster Abbey. It was a huge success. Ibbs and Tillett were now appointed her sole agents.

Roy Henderson took her in hand, and encouraged greater liveliness in her singing: a quality certainly there in her private conversation, where she even had a tendency to ribaldry. Elgar's *The Apostles*, *The Kingdom*, and *The Dream of Gerontius* were in her repertoire, as well as Mendelssohn's *Elijah*, Handel's *Messiah*, Dvořák's *Requiem*, Bach's *B Minor Mass* and *Christmas Oratorio*, Brahms' *Alto Rhapsody* and *Four Serious Songs*, various *Lieder*, and a great variety of folk songs. Many of these were recorded and are still available. She made friends with the contralto Nancy Evans, who had a similar repertoire.

Kathleen was still noticing intermittent pain in her left breast, which even spread down her arm, but she did nothing about it. During wartime she was subject to considerable stress, travelling all over the UK in difficult conditions. She was very busy, with no time to give to herself.

She was contracted to the Columbia Gramophone Company, whose artistic director was Walter Legge, who offered helpful criticism but whose technical expertise was lacking, and who seems to have been somewhat inappropriately flirtatious. She then transferred to Decca. But before this she recorded songs by Purcell and Mendelssohn accompanied by Gerald Moore, which were highly praised. Another accompanist was Phyllis Spurr, who became a congenial companion.

In December 1945, after the Second World War, but while there were still serious shortages and privations, she gave 17 performances of *Messiah*, from Blackpool to Dunfermline. Her fame was spreading, but at what cost to her health? A new challenge was an invitation to create the role of Lucretia in Benjamin Britten's new opera *The Rape of Lucretia*, with a libretto by Ronald Duncan and ultimately based on Shakespeare's poem. After the end of the war, in 1946, the country opera house at Glyndebourne in Sussex was reopened, and plans were made to stage *Lucretia* there. This was a huge challenge, which Kathleen rose to magnificently. *The Times* wrote:

…*in Miss Kathleen Ferrier, the opera has a protagonist who was able, without strain, to present tragedy with a splendid voice and great dignity of bearing.[3]*

Later that year the company toured round England and Scotland for two months, but sadly the provincial tour was not a success. It drew much bigger audiences in Holland, where Kathleen joined Benjamin Britten and Peter Pears, and was hosted by Peter Diamand, the Dutch impresario. The enthusiastic response of the Dutch audiences made up to some extent for the lukewarm reception in Britain. But Kathleen put her heart and soul into it, even managing a top A, which she had thought beyond her range. Her sister Winifred wrote:

Kathleen played the part of Lucretia many times. There were probably not many people who realised what it demanded of her. Few penetrated her defences or saw through the face she showed the world and perhaps none saw far. 'Last night Tarquinius ravished me And took his peace from me…' In this opera to sing these words demands a high order of emotional control, but when their meaning has personal significance, the strain can be almost intolerable.

Perhaps the real explanation of that 'Top A' lies in its symbolic revelation of how she dealt with the deep problems of her life.[4]

Winifred does not however tell us whether or not Kathleen herself was 'ravished'. We shall never know.

After a short holiday in Denmark, Kathleen returned to a packed schedule in autumn 1946. She was booked by Glyndebourne for Gluck's *Orfeo ed Euridice*. This demanded greater acting technique than she possessed, and she worked extremely hard to perfect the role. The opening night on 19th June 1947 was a triumph: Kathleen took 16 curtain calls, and the critics were ecstatic. Kathleen herself was however still dissatisfied with her own acting.

The next major event was the inaugural Edinburgh International Festival, held in August 1947, where Kathleen first sang with Bruno Walter, who was looking for a contralto to sing Mahler's *Das Lied von der Erde* (he had already recruited Peter Pears to sing the tenor part). There was controversy about performing a German work so soon after the war, but Walter (who had spent the war years in America) was very impressed when Kathleen auditioned for the part, and the critics were almost all favourable. Walter (aged 71) wrote of his first meeting with Kathleen (aged 34):

> *She came in, not shy and not too bold, but in modest self-confidence, dressed in a kind of Salzburg costume, a dirndl, looking young and lovely, pure and earnest, simple and noble, and the room seemed to become brighter for the charm of her presence. She had the charm of a child and the dignity of a lady.[5]*

They rehearsed in Kathleen's flat in London with the piano, and in Edinburgh with the Vienna Philharmonic Orchestra. Since the Edinburgh Festival was an international event, Kathleen was now inundated with invitations to sing from all over the world. At home, her sister Winifred had to move to be nearer her work, and Kathleen needed a secretary and someone to look after her father while she was away, so Paddy Jewett, who was studying to be a soprano, was appointed — with great success.

On New Year's Day 1947 she set sail for New York, with the elderly John Tillett as her manager. They had a luxurious voyage, greatly enjoyed by Kathleen. They were greeted in New York by a press conference, and she indulged in ration-free shopping, though she herself was liable for her travel and accommodation expenses. Managing her money was difficult. Again she sang *Das Lied von der Erde*, with Walter conducting. The audience was appreciative but the reviews were mixed. Her next performance was broadcast coast to coast, and was better appreciated. She continued with an ambitious programme, including Chicago. But financially she made little, after all her expenses and income tax were paid.

Back home, the next date was Elgar's *Dream of Gerontius*, under Malcolm Sargent at the Albert Hall, when she was presented to Princess Elizabeth, Princess Margaret and the Duke of Edinburgh. A tour of Holland followed, managed by Peter Diamand, who overcame initial lukewarm interest and organized a successful tour.

During this year her agent John Tillett, who had accompanied her to America, died, and she was concerned that his wife Emmie might be lonely. They struck up a friendship. Kathleen herself was also lonely, and during 1947 her marriage to Bert was finally annulled. Bert had been away in the Army during the war. Her last reference to him in her diary was on 25th January 1945 when she had lunch with him. There was no bitterness, but it had never been a success from the start. Bert then remarried.

As for Kathleen, she had a fairly long-term relationship with Rick Davies, an antique dealer from Liverpool, young and good-looking (a photograph of the pair of them in 1948 was published in Christopher Fifield's book).[6] Her diaries mention him many times: the first in February 1943, when 'Rick rang up from Liverpool',[7] and the last on 17th February 1952 when she records: 'Rick coming'. He often sent her flowers, and they met for many meals together. He also came to a number of her performances. On 16th February 1945 she records 'Rick came to concert. Grand.'[8] In July 1948 she went on holiday with Rick in Northern Ireland, where food was plentiful and off the ration. But she wrote to Winifred in June 1950, after another brief holiday with him in Zurich:

> I guess I'm meant to be a lone she-wolf. I don't mind him for a buddy for two days, then I've had enough and want to retire behind an iron curtain and not have to listen and make conversation! Fickle, that's me.[9]

Perhaps she protested too much here, and might really have wanted to be closer. It seems that her frantic programme of professional engagements hampered her personal life, and the two never married. There was another relationship later, which also did not mature into marriage. According to Bernie Hammond the man concerned, before marrying someone else, returned all her letters, which she then burnt, crying floods of tears. Kathleen envied women who were able to marry and have children, and childlessness is a known risk factor for breast cancer. Her sister Winifred was close, but with most people she was reserved. The soprano Joan Cross characterized her as a private person, and yet she could be wildly exuberant with friends.

In August 1948 Kathleen appeared at the Promenade concerts, and again at the Edinburgh Festival, where she gave a recital with Gerald Moore as accompanist, and sang in the Bach *B Minor Mass* under Malcolm Sargent, now Sir Malcolm. Further engagements followed in Denmark, Sheffield, Manchester and Bradford. Back in London again she felt a pain in her breast, and went to St Mary's Hospital, Paddington, for a check-up, but was reassured that all was well. Was it in fact? Did the doctors really do a thorough examination? Did she receive a mammogram? We have no means of knowing.

Kathleen was reminded of another loss when she received a congratulatory letter from her old headmistress, Miss Gardner. Kathleen replied: '…my great regret is that I had to leave so early. In my particular work, how grateful I should have been for fluent French, German and Italian…'[10] But her older brother had to come first in the family's list of priorities.

After more tours of Holland and Ireland Kathleen left again for America, this time on her own, in February 1949. With no manager (since Tillett had died) she had to deal with all administrative problems by herself. The first was concerning her accompanist, Arpad Sandor. Previously he had been cheerful and reliable: this year he was erratic and unreliable, and also demanding higher fees, which she had to pay out of her own income. When she confronted him over his poor playing, he told her his wife was ill, but then his wife turned up, and it transpired that Sandor himself was the patient: he was suffering from serious mental illness. The realization made Kathleen conduct their rehearsals in a different spirit, but finally in Chicago Sandor broke down completely and had to give up. His place was taken at short notice by a Canadian pianist, John Newmark, who turned out to be ideal. However, the stress of travel and fatigue was mounting after three months in America alone without a manager. Also, perhaps tempted by luxurious off-ration food, she was now overweight at 12 stone (another risk factor for breast cancer).

While in America Kathleen was able to spend some time with Bruno Walter on their Edinburgh programme. She also went to Havana, Cuba, where a concert with John Newmark drew an ecstatic, lengthy review in a Havana newspaper. This is only an extract (translated from the Spanish):

Kathleen Ferrier is more than a mere singer, she is a real miracle, a happy blend of admirable musicality and vocal quality, of angel-like purity and delicious timbre, of technique and schooling, of finesse and nuances, of overwhelming tone production and sureness: elegance, wonderful restraint, exquisite diction, flawless phrasing, unique gift for voice projection, effortless, like breathing and talking, noble and dignified expression without any exaggeration or false pathos, a control whose proud nobility yet contains great human sweetness, with it a quite unique personal charm in appearance and with all this (much too little to do her justice) the greatest gift to move her listeners that we have ever found in a singer.[11]

After the concert the British Ambassador invited Kathleen and John Newmark to dinner, after which Kathleen accepted a Havana cigar. (She had smoked moderately for years — another risk factor for cancer. She also drank alcohol in moderation — as one would expect in her circumstances, where post-concert hospitality was the rule.) She then took a short holiday in Miami and sang in more concerts before returning home.

Her next challenge was the opera *Orfeo ed Euridice* by Gluck at the Holland Festival. She persuaded Winifred to come to the opening night, to which Rick Davies also came: Kathleen was seriously considering becoming engaged to him. *Orfeo* was a huge success, followed by a banquet. Following *Orfeo* came Britten's *Spring Symphony*, with the contralto part written specifically for Kathleen. This performance, with the Concertgebouw Orchestra, was very well received. But by now Kathleen was utterly exhausted. She and Winifred went for a week's holiday in Switzerland, but Kathleen spent much of the time resting.

Her next commitment was to the Salzburg festival, where she was worried that her German pronunciation of *Das Lied von der Erde* would not come up to scratch. But she triumphed all the same. Then, at the Edinburgh Festival, she gave performances on six consecutive evenings, four with Bruno Walter at the piano. Alan Blyth wrote for *The Gramophone*: 'Walter's very personal and positive support obviously pushes Ferrier to give of her very best. What a remarkable partnership it was.'[12] Finally they managed to overcome contractual complications with Decca and recorded Mahler's *Kindertotenlieder* together with Columbia, to their very great satisfaction.

Then followed another hectic round of concerts in Scandinavia: Copenhagen, Oslo, and Stockholm. During this tour however she suffered from pains in her neck and right arm, written off as 'rheumatism', and somewhat eased by massage, but increasing in frequency. Did this already signal metastatic cancer? After a brief break back in London, Kathleen was off to Paris for a recital in the Salle Gaveau, and then on 21st December to America, where John Newmark was once again her pianist. On 4th January 1950 her tour started: Nashville, Tennessee, preceded by a 24-hour train journey. There followed a hectic tour involving continuous travel for 20 days, and then a return visit to Chicago. After that, New Mexico, and Los Angeles, where she stayed (in his absence) at Bruno Walter's home in Beverly Hills, where she had a luxurious fortnight's holiday.

More work followed in America, and in San Francisco she met Marian Anderson, an African American contralto with a huge vocal range: for Kathleen this was a great thrill. Further concerts were in Chicago, New Brunswick, New York, and New Jersey. She returned to her Hampstead flat in April 1950 to find it beautifully redecorated by Paddy and her father William. She made a brief visit to Glyndebourne, where she sang in Bach's *St Matthew Passion*: then off to Amsterdam and back to London for Mahler's *Kindertotenlieder* at the Albert Hall.

Plans were made for recordings with John Newmark, who was brought over from America via Paris by Decca, who paid his expenses. He arrived in July and they recorded Schumann's *Frauenliebe und Leben,* and Brahms' *Four Serious Songs*. Later, Kathleen went to Vienna (still occupied by Allied troops) and Zurich for further performances; then to Milan, where she sang the Bach *B Minor Mass* under Herbert von Karajan: her fellow soloist was the soprano Elisabeth Schwarzkopf.

Back in London she again felt pain in her breast, shoulder, and back, but her doctor gave her a clean bill of health. Once more we have to wonder why. She now needed a rest before her third Edinburgh Festival appearance, where she sang Brahms' *Alto Rhapsody*, conducted by Fritz Busch. In September she sang in a concert raising funds for the United Nations with Benjamin Britten and Peter Pears.

In November she sang in Manchester, and then in Holland for three weeks, with Gerald Moore as accompanist. She loved singing with him, but complained that he was expensive: she was paying his fees. Another three months followed in America, and then back to London, thence to Scotland, but home for Christmas, where she had to tackle a backlog of letters. She had not much chance of catching up: she was off again to Amsterdam for a season of *Orfeo ed Euridice*.

More performances followed in various European capitals. While in Rome she heard that her father had had a stroke, and was unlikely to live long. She wanted to go home, but was dissuaded by Winifred, who came to Paris for her final concert on 23rd January 1951. Further plans were made for the months ahead, but Kathleen's health took a turn for the worse. Luckily before that Bernadine Hammond, who was also a trained nurse, was engaged as Secretary, taking the place of Paddy, who left to get married. While Bernadine (Bernie) settled in, Kathleen left for a tour of northern England with the Hallé Orchestra and Sir John Barbirolli as conductor.

A great occasion was Kathleen's début (under Barbirolli) with Chausson's *Poème de l'Amour et de la Mer*, which she had long been working on (especially the French pronunciation). It was a huge success, culminating in a BBC broadcast from Manchester. There were also concert performances of *Orfeo ed Euridice*. She stayed with the Barbirollis throughout the tour, at the end of which Barbirolli confessed that he had ignored the symptoms of appendicitis: he now sought treatment. But Barbirolli was not satisfied with a mere concert performance of *Orfeo ed Euridice*, and made plans for a run at the Royal Opera House, Covent Garden.

On her return to Hampstead on 13th March, to find all neat and tidy owing to Bernie's labours, she looked very tired, and asked Bernie to have a look at a lump in her breast. It was clear to Bernie what it was, but Kathleen did not see a doctor until 24th March, after she had completed a tour of Holland and Germany. She was admitted to University College Hospital on 9th April and had a mastectomy of her left breast on 10th April.

Kathleen did not want the public to know about her operation: cancer was something one did not mention in those days. Waiting for the operation she rested, painted pictures and walked on Hampstead Heath. Several concerts had to be cancelled: 'I should have gone [to the doctor] earlier but I haven't been home for months', she confessed in a letter to Benita Cress in America.[13] She wrote to John Newmark: 'It's lovely to have it over, because I had been worried for a bit and had been abroad all the time, and couldn't do anything there — and it's miserable to sing and feel lousy, isn't it?'[14]

On 22nd April, her 39th birthday, she was still in hospital undergoing radio-therapy: she celebrated with a party, inviting notable guests including Benjamin Britten and Peter Pears. After three weeks she was discharged home, and continued daily treatment as an outpatient. Barbirolli and his wife, the oboist Evelyn Roth-well, were visitors: Barbirolli insisted on cooking a meal for her. They sometimes played chamber music: Kathleen now had a new Steinway grand piano.

After her treatment she took a short holiday in Alfriston, Sussex, with painting as her main recreation. She was also studying Brahms' songs in preparation for the Edinburgh Festival. She only took three months off before returning to the concert platform: first with the *B Minor Mass*, then *Orfeo ed Euridice* in Holland. Mahler's Second Symphony followed, conducted by Otto Klemperer (whose stormy behaviour was disconcerting). But Kathleen was tired out, and she was having pains in her back.

When she returned to London she had a course of radiotherapy on her back. Even so, she travelled to Liverpool after treatment for a performance the same evening. Next she went to King's Lynn, then Birmingham, for further recitals. At the Edinburgh Festival she gave two recitals with Bruno Walter and one with Barbirolli. On the way back to London she even stopped at Marple and Ilkley for further recitals. But her doctor then told her that she must not perform any more that autumn: she had to cancel a tour of America.

Then in October she performed *The Enchantress* by Sir Arthur Bliss, who reported that she was in a happy mood. In November she sang with Barbirolli at the reopening of the Free Trade Hall in Manchester, to an audience including the Queen. She stayed with the Barbirollis in Manchester, but back home went again to University College Hospital, where she was prescribed more radiotherapy. After a long rest and Christmas at home she started singing again on 7th January 1952, with *Four Serious Songs* by Brahms at the Albert Hall with Sir Malcolm Sargent, followed by the Chausson *Poème de l'Amour et de la Mer* at the Royal Festival Hall with Gaston Poulet. Then she was off again for a gruelling tour of the north and west of England, culminating in a partnership with Benjamin Britten and Peter Pears to raise funds for the English Opera Group.

But Kathleen was not well: Bernie came and rescued her from a hotel in Nottingham, though afterwards Kathleen told her she was fine. In fact she was not at all fine, and when she returned to London she had to go back to hospital for more radiotherapy. Apparently her doctor, Dr Reggie Hilton, who owned a Stradivarius violin, frequently joined her and the Barbirollis for chamber music, rather than to examine her. It seems that this may have confused the therapeutic relationship. One can only wish that he had diagnosed her breast cancer much earlier than he did.

After her treatment had finished, as a celebration she took Bernie to see Sir John Gielgud in *Much Ado About Nothing*. Gielgud also visited her. Kathleen then busied herself with undertaking home repairs and creating a garden, which she much enjoyed. On 30th March came a performance of Bach's *St Matthew Passion* at the Royal Albert Hall. Her back pains returned, but she was cheered by a letter from Newmark, telling her that her recording with him of *Frauenliebe und Leben* had gained the Grand Prix des Disques (a French award). She replied telling him about her plans for concerts, and also that she had been asked to sing at a private party for Princess Margaret and the Queen Mother on 30th April.

Meanwhile she had more work in Manchester with Barbirolli. Back in London, it was clear that Kathleen's health was seriously deteriorating. She finally sought a second opinion from Sir Stanford Cade, who suggested the injection of androgenic hormones, which Kathleen refused since this would probably have affected her

101

voice. But she did accept further radiotherapy. On her birthday in April Barbirolli organized a party and arrived with a huge birthday cake. After another concert at the Free Trade Hall in Manchester, Kathleen departed for Vienna, which was still occupied by the Russians. Over six days she made a recording with Victor Olof. Then followed Mahler's *Das Lied von der Erde* with Bruno Walter, and lunch at the British Embassy. But by now Kathleen was in a lot of pain, in spite of which she managed to record, with an immense effort, a set of three Mahler songs with Bruno Walter.

Back in London she rested for three days, then off she went to Newcastle, and back to the Festival Hall on 28th May for a concert with Sargent conducting Britten's *Spring Symphony*. Then she spent two weeks at the Aldeburgh Festival, run by Britten and Pears, where she sang in a performance of Britten's *Abraham and Isaac*. She took a further holiday in Cornwall, and then a weekend in the country house of Burton Paritt, next door to David Bowes Lyon, brother of the Queen Mother, who was having the Queen to dine with him. David took the opportunity to ask Kathleen to sing for the occasion, which she did.

Afterwards in Hampstead Barbirolli asked Kathleen if she would sing in *Orfeo ed Euridice* at Covent Garden. In spite of her poor health, Kathleen was excited at the prospect. It was to be sung in English and titled *Orpheus*. She would have to learn the English words, but knew the music well. Barbirolli and Kathleen got together to rewrite the English version, and prepare for the production, scheduled for February 1953. But first came the Edinburgh Festival, her sixth. She was feeling better, not working so hard, and also able to rest from hospital visits. At the Festival she gave her first performance of the *Liebeslieder* waltzes by Brahms, which were a huge success. Again she gave various recitals on the way back home, in spite of arduous train journeys and severe back pain. On 5th October she gave a recital with Britten and Pears in the Victoria and Albert Museum.

She had a difficult time that October as she was plagued with anonymous phone calls and spiteful tricks. The perpetrators turned out to be female fans, who had felt rejected. Their campaign presented further worry for Kathleen. By the time she had made a series of recordings with the London Philharmonic Orchestra under Sir Adrian Boult she was totally exhausted.

But Kathleen kept going, with a concert in Antrim in October, and again for royalty on 3rd November at the Chapel Royal in Windsor. Then on 4th November she appeared at the Festival Hall in a recital with Gerald Moore, and again on 23rd November for *Das Lied von der Erde* with the London Symphony Orchestra conducted by Josef Krips, with Richard Lewis singing the tenor solo. Against all advice she made a tour of the Lake District with the *Messiah* in December, followed by a concert in Carlisle. On returning to Hampstead she found food parcels from America and a pile of Christmas mail, including a letter from the Prime Minister offering her the CBE, which greatly delighted her. On 23rd December she sang in a Christmas *Messiah*, and on New Year's Eve celebrated her CBE with a group of special friends.

In 1953 the main item on Kathleen's programme was *Orpheus* at Covent Garden, for which the opening night was 3rd February. Rehearsals for *Orpheus* occupied much of Kathleen's time during January. The production was excellent, with Frederick Ashton as choreographer/producer and Svetlana Beriosova from Sadler's Wells as principal dancer. Kathleen was increasingly frail, and had difficulty walking, with pain in her legs and back. But on stage she was miraculously transformed, and moved beautifully. Her daily radiotherapy treatments somewhat eased the pain, but must have made her extremely tired, and the cumulative effect of all her radiotherapy must have been serious. Perhaps her radiologist was not worried about the long-term adverse effects, knowing her prognosis was so poor. Her name was Gwen Hilton: was she related to Kathleen's doctor Reggie Hilton? Kathleen also consulted a laryngologist about the effects of an oophorectomy (removal of the ovaries), which was offered as well. Her consultant James Ivor Griffiths reported:

I told her that the long-term effects on the cancer would be negligible but that the effect on her voice might be disastrous. I had quite a bit of experience of the effect of hormones on the voice and I told her that it would at least alter the character of the voice. She said that she regarded her voice as a divine gift and would go to the grave with the voice as it had been given her. She had this overpowering desire to sing in Orpheus and said that she would go ahead. I then had a consultation with Sir John Barbirolli and Sir David Webster and I told them that I was doubtful whether she could complete the four performances. However, we decided to let her carry on.[15] **

The first performance of *Orpheus* was a triumph, and drew superlative press reviews. Even Kathleen's movements on stage were praised. But halfway through the second performance she was attacked by a terrible pain in her left thigh, and she could not move. In spite of this she continued singing, leaning against scenery, and helped by another member of the cast, who was able to support her when she had to exit from the stage. She managed to stagger back on stage to finish her part, and her laryngologist who had been waiting in the wings gave her a morphia injection so that she could return again to receive the applause.

Afterwards she returned home on a stretcher and was made comfortable by Bernie. The next day an X-ray revealed a broken femur. Once more she went back to University College Hospital (UCH) as an inpatient for daily radiotherapy. The two remaining performances of *Orpheus* had to be cancelled: there had been no understudy for her part. She also missed her investiture as a CBE. The steps up to

---

** I should add that at the time of writing hormone treatment in the form of the drug Tamoxifen is still being widely prescribed even as a breast cancer preventative, with no warning to patients of the possible effect on the voice, which is not listed in the *British National Formulary*. Even for amateur singers this can be seriously upsetting, as I know personally. *HG*

her door in Frognal Mansions were now impossible for her to manage, so Bernie and Winifred managed to find a ground floor flat in nearby St John's Wood. Her friend Ruth Draper organized a makeover of the garden and weekly visits from a gardener to keep it in order. Kathleen was delighted with her new home.

Further singing engagements that year were cancelled, though Kathleen still planned to sing at the Edinburgh Festival. She made excellent progress, and was soon getting about and even making cakes. She also took up her painting again. A physiotherapist visited in the evenings; the Barbirollis came to dinner—and also prepared the food. She even ventured out to dinner with nearby Hamish Hamilton, where the guest of honour was Princess Margaret. But while there she had a nausea attack. This signalled a downward spiral, and on 22nd May she went back to UCH for further treatment. She deteriorated rapidly, but rallied sufficiently to consent to the dreaded oophorectomy, after which her strength came back to some extent, though she had to cancel her Edinburgh Festival performance with Bruno Walter.

Kathleen's agent Emmie Tillett, realizing that Kathleen had not much longer to live, proposed to the Royal Philharmonic Society that they should award her their Gold Medal. They agreed, and the award was made to her, still in UCH. Another operation was proposed, and accepted: an adrenalectomy (removal of the adrenal glands), which was done at Westminster Hospital. Her cancer had now spread to her skeleton and Kathleen felt she had nothing to lose. Her pain certainly decreased, but the desired result of arresting the cancer was not achieved. Her voice, however, seemed as beautiful as ever when Barbirolli visited.

Kathleen then asked to go back to UCH, where she had so many friends, and this was achieved at the end of September. She died there on 8th October 1953 at the age of only 41. Her body was cremated at Golders Green Crematorium and a rose bed planted for her in the Garden of Remembrance. On 24th November a service was held in Southwark Cathedral, presided over by the Bishop of Croydon, Cuthbert Bardsley, an old friend, attended by over 1,000 people. Other services followed in different places. The Kathleen Ferrier Cancer Research Fund was launched, and the Kathleen Ferrier Chair of Clinical Oncology was created at UCH. The Kathleen Ferrier Memorial Scholarship was founded, for both sexes and all voices, administered by the Royal Philharmonic Society. Many recordings of her work are still available, so we can marvel at the beauty of her voice and her interpretations of a wide range of music.

Particularly notable are the reminiscences of musicians themselves, collected together in *Kathleen Ferrier: a Memoir*, edited by Neville Cardus, where Sir John Barbirolli, Benjamin Britten, Roy Henderson, Gerald Moore, and Bruno Walter write eloquently about their memories of her and her work. As Roy Henderson says:

Many accompanists will claim the honour of having played for her, but her greatest thrill came from her recitals with Bruno Walter and Gerald Moore. She never debased herself by singing trash. She was a true musician.[16]

So what can we conclude about why Kathleen developed breast cancer? She herself always thought that the accidental knock on her breast by her husband was the original cause: this is unlikely but possible. Perhaps the main difficulty in her life was her failure to maintain a long-term relationship with a partner. Being childless was another risk factor, and we can only imagine what a wonderful mother she might have been. But her hectic life as a soloist must have been extremely stressful, travelling all over the world at a time when it was still a gruelling experience even after the war was over. Financial problems dogged her, with different currencies and regulations in every country she visited, and the obligation to pay her accompanist out of her own fees. The early death of her mother was another crisis for her. Although on the surface she was a bubbly person, and great fun to be with, she rarely shared her innermost thoughts. We can only be grateful that she was able to sing so beautifully at a time when recordings were beginning to be reliable, so that her legacy is still with us.

Select Bibliography

Paul Campion: *Ferrier: A Career Recorded* (Julia MacRae, London, 1992)

Neville Cardus: *Kathleen Ferrier 1912–1953: a Memoir* (Hamish Hamilton, London, 1954)

Winifred Ferrier: *The Life of Kathleen Ferrier* (Readers Union, Hamish Hamilton, London, 1956)

Christopher Fifield (ed.):   *Letters and Diaries of Kathleen Ferrier* (The Boydell Press, Woodbridge, 2003)

Maurice Leonard: *The Life of Kathleen Ferrier 1912–1953* (Century Hutchinson Ltd, London, 1988; Futura edition, 1989)

Peter Lethbridge: *Kathleen Ferrier* (Red Lion Lives, Cassell & Co. Ltd, London, 1959)

Notes

1. Leonard, p. 16.
2. *ibid.*, p. 55.
3. *ibid.*, p. 84.
4. Ferrier, p. 77.
5. Leonard, p. 98.
6. Fifield, photos between pp. 148 and 149.
7. *ibid.*, p. 224.
8. *ibid.*, p. 122.
9. *ibid.*, p. 122.
10. *ibid.*, p. 58.
11. Leonard, p. 13.
12. *ibid.*, p. 145.
13. Fifield, p. 147.
14. *ibid.*, p. 150.
15. Leonard, p. 229.
16. Cardus, p. 74.

Joan Eardley

LIKE KATHLEEN FERRIER, JOAN EARDLEY died at the height of a creative career. She was the first child of Captain William Eardley, who was billeted in Glasgow during his army service in the First World War, and met his Scottish wife there: Irena Morrison. Joan was born in 1921, not in Scotland but on a dairy farm in Warnham, near Horsham in West Sussex, where her parents struggled to make ends meet and finally gave up. Her father gained employment in the Ministry of Agriculture in Lincoln, but was still suffering from the late effects of being gassed in the trenches, and in deep depression committed suicide in 1929.

When this happened Joan was only eight, her sister Patricia six. (Joan too was to experience depression in later life.) Her mother had already moved the family to Blackheath, near Greenwich Park in London, to join her own mother and her sister Sybil, a leading light in the women's rights movement. Great aunts visited, and Joan went to a private school, paid for by the aunts, where her growing talent for art was encouraged. On leaving school she spent two terms at an art school in Blackheath, and then another two at Goldsmith's College of Art. Late in 1939, to avoid the threatened London bombing, the family moved again to Glasgow, and Joan continued her education at the Glasgow School of Art, where the staff were few owing to the war, and materials were in short supply.

Joan made a special friend of a fellow student, Margot Sandeman. She was lucky to have Hugh Adam Crawford as her teacher of drawing and painting. Interestingly, he talks about an artist needing to break down the typical Scottish inhibition:

> If you want to be a good painter, and I mean one who matters beyond the ordinary kind of success with people around you, you have to be prepared to break down some kind of barrier within yourself. In Scotland we are all born with a constraint of this kind — we get it with our mother's milk. Somehow we have to enter into another plane of living, to break through, or away from, Scottish morality — the vulgar idea of Godliness. There can't be any 'good' or 'bad' or 'yes' or 'no'. You have to accept that there's a kind of necessity before which everything has to go down.[1]

Little of Joan's work from this period survives, an exception being her diploma self-portrait, which was actually bought by Crawford himself. The work also won her the Sir James Guthrie Prize for portraiture.

Her home was in the Bearsden district of Glasgow, near the countryside, and she explored the West Highland Way, the Isle of Arran, and Loch Lomond, with Margot Sandeman. During the Second World War young women were required either to train as teachers or to be called up for the services. Although Joan did enrol at Jordanhill Teacher Training College, she decided to quit teaching in favour of a 'reserved' occupation as a joiner's labourer in a boat-building yard. At the same time she continued painting. Works from this period include *The Mixer Men*: two workmen with a cement mixer. Her 'war work' included painting camouflage on boat hulls. She was also sending paintings to exhibitions in Glasgow and Edinburgh. Margot moved to Bletchley Park in Buckinghamshire to work as a code-breaker during the war, and Joan visited her there.

After the war Joan moved to London, where she was very short of money, but managed somehow. Although London was exciting in many ways, Joan was also homesick, and had depressive episodes. She wrote: '...a terrible helpless hopeless feeling has come upon me—everything seems to be such a dreadful unending struggle.'[2] But she showed paintings in various exhibitions, including a West of Scotland show of young artists. She was elected a member of the Scottish Artists in 1948, and the *Glasgow Herald* wrote:

Among the West of Scotland painters Joan Eardley, with two large interiors, hinting at both Gilman and the Colquhoun-MacBride [MacBryde] school, is noteworthy. There is a certain dusky confusion about both works but the colour is bold and the drawing strong and personal.[3]

But Joan herself, when she saw this, commented to Margot:

It's really a terrific joke the funny things that are about you in the paper—you a pseudo classical & me with works hinting at Gilman & Colquhoun & McBride [MacBryde]—people I have never even thought of when I've been painting. If they said Gauguin they might have been a bit nearer![4]

Joan was encouraged by her mother to apply for a place at the Hospitalfield School of Art, in a large house near Arbroath, which ran a post-graduate summer school. She made many drawings and paintings locally, especially of Arbroath Harbour, but was not allowed to paint the interior of the magnificent house with its stock of antique treasures. While at Hospitalfield Joan made friends with Angus Neil, a joiner-cum-painter: the relationship grew into something like that between an older sister and younger brother (he was three years younger). He was lonely (as was she) and had mental problems: to some extent Joan looked after him, though he also modelled for her a good deal.

The warden of Hospitalfield, James Cowie RSA, had a very prescriptive view of art that cut across Joan's perspective, but they managed to work together all the same, and she was offered a post-graduate year at the Glasgow School of Art, after which she won two scholarships that enabled her to work for several months in France and Italy.

While abroad Joan wrote to her friend Margot and her mother about her experiences in Italy, with great enthusiasm but also recounting periods of depression. These were to recur during the rest of her life. In Italy she reflected on the difference in the effect of sunlight between south and north:

> ...here, in this southern climate, the brilliant sun shining down upon the dusty white earth is reflected back so that there are no shadows on figures, and the shadows on build-ings are shadows of lightness and colour, not shadows of darkness. But in the North, the sun shines upon earth which is dark, or upon green grass, and is absorbed, not reflected upwards — and so the people in our part of the world are dark and light together.[5]

But she also felt frustrated:

> The trouble is not being able to speak the beastly language — you can't converse and get to know the peasants who speak to you. There is always this stumbling block — to me a very great one.[6]

She visited several galleries in Florence, Padua, and Venice, which gave her the opportunity to study old masters — Fra Angelico, Giotto, Masaccio, Piero della Francesca — and in the hill-town of Assisi she made many landscape drawings. She also visited the coast and drew fishermen mending nets. Next she visited Paris, which she found somewhat disappointing, until she met up with an Australian woman she had known earlier, also a painter, who insisted on Joan visiting the galleries with her. There was an exhibition from Munich, where the Rembrandts took her breath away, and she was also tremendously taken with Goya, Rubens, El Greco, Botticelli, and Dürer.

Joan then returned to Italy, first to Venice and then to Florence. She was in a melancholy mood when leaving Italy for Glasgow: '...And here I am, leaving and I haven't made *one* painting — a bundle of little things which are just simply nothing — and a few drawings'.[7] But in fact the work she brought back from Italy was warmly received when she exhibited it in the School of Art Museum in Glasgow in October 1949. Alick Sturrock wrote in the *Glasgow Herald*: 'Among the most outstanding are a charcoal study of an old peasant woman sewing, wrapped in a ruckled shawl, her knobbly fingers drawing the eye irresistibly...'[8]

Joan then set up a modest studio at the top of a building in Cochrane Street, opposite the Glasgow City Chambers. Angus Neil lived nearby. Her most famous paintings and drawings from this period are those of the street children, whom she bribed to sit for her with various inducements including sweets and a box of toys. Further subjects were horses and carts, still seen in the centre of Glasgow. Groups of children continued to fascinate her. Influences were Van Gogh, Pablo Picasso and Paul Klee, among others. She read left-wing journals such as the *New Statesman*, and engaged with both social realism and abstraction in her work.

Margot Sandeman had long been a close friend, to whom many letters were written, but when Margot married James Robson, Dorothy Steel, another young painter, took her place as a companion. In 1951 she and Joan went to France together, staying in a village near Toulouse for several months. The influence of Van Gogh had long been evident in her work, and now became even more apparent.

Back in Glasgow she resumed her studies of street children, and was also an ardent music lover and concert-goer, having a special affection for the music of Benjamin Britten. She found a better studio in St James's Road, Townhead, still in Glasgow. A famous and moving painting from this period is the *Sleeping Nude*, with her friend Angus Neil as the subject. There is no evidence of any kind of a sexual relationship with him—indeed, Joan's sexual partners were always women—but the work drew unwelcome comment from the press, implying that they had an illicit relationship, which must have been upsetting. However, her friendship with Angus offered her some protection against unwanted attention from other men. He often posed for her, though never again naked.

The main subjects for her work at this period were still street children, strikingly and lovingly portrayed, for which she soon became renowned, and down-to-earth tenement landscapes, for instance *Tenements and Washing*. There were several entitled *A Glasgow Boy*. The *Glasgow Herald* reviewed one show:

> *Her portraits of children, of which there are several examples in the present show, small solemn urchins who gaze upon the world with round eyes and open mouths, are at once lively and still. These heads are truly remarkable. In what is probably the most difficult branch of portraiture it is uncommon to find a combination of skill, acute observation and sympathetic truth.[9]*

Meanwhile Joan's personal life was developing. After Margot Sandeman's marriage she had other friends, and she became very close to Audrey Walker, whom she first met in Glasgow in 1952. Her husband Allan Walker was later Sheriff Principal of Glasgow and Lanarkshire. Audrey played the violin, but on her marriage gave up ideas of becoming a professional musician, concentrating instead on photography. Joan was invited to the Walkers' country retreat near Selkirk, where she painted several interiors, notably *The Music Stand*.

Even more inspiring was her discovery of Catterline on the east coast south of Aberdeen. This was the area that her grandfather came from. She discovered the place, a small fishing community south of Stonehaven, in 1950 when she exhibited her work in Aberdeen. It is still an unspoiled village. An art teacher, Annette Roper, daughter of Joan's Aberdeen hosts, showed her the place, and later bought a derelict building, the Watch House, in Catterline and renovated it to make a studio where Joan came to work for increasingly long periods. She bought a Lambretta motor scooter, so she could get to Catterline from the local station.

In 1954 she found another cottage of her own, No. 1 Catterline, primitive but satisfying: 'This is a strange place—it always excites me,' she wrote in a letter.[10]

Joan's experience as a joiner came in handy as she set to work with Angus Neil to repair and renovate the building. There was no electricity, no indoor sanitation or running water: buckets of water had to be carried up a steep slope every day. When it all became too much in 1959 Joan moved to No. 18, which did have sanitation, but she kept No. 1 as a studio. She divided her time between Glasgow (Townhead) and Catterline. The Samson children in Townhead were her particular favourites, and they would tell her all the local news and gossip.

In 1955 she had her first solo exhibition in London, and was also elected an Associate of the Royal Scottish Academy. Her work was now becoming known fairly widely: a gem from this period is *Cornfield at Nightfall*, portraying a row of cottages with a foreground of haystacks and a rising moon. But around this time she started to suffer neck pains, apparently from a slipped disc—no doubt partly from continually drawing standing up out of doors. She was fitted with a surgical collar, and started recording views with a camera, as an *aide mémoire* for later paintings. But neck problems did not curtail her work: she went on working outdoors, even in winter. In December 1955 she wrote:

> What a night, and what a morning—storm still raging like anything—paintings and photos all out of date. The sea is all whiteness, right far out over the bay, and the bay all thick yellow foam—the tide is out at the moment, so the waves are breaking enormously—far out. When it comes in I guess there won't be much room for any poor person that would want to stand on the pathway—and I don't know if I shall be able to keep my easel standing.[11]

Her stormy seascapes are among the finest ever painted by a Scottish artist: four are in public galleries, for instance *The Wave* at the Scottish National Gallery of Modern Art. She also loved the paraphernalia of fishing—*Drying Salmon Nets* stands out—and the local landscapes. She wrote to Margot:

> I've got a series of paintings going at the end of my old cottage. I never seem to find that I want to move. It's a handy spot as no-one comes near and I can work away undisturbed. I just go on from one painting to another—just the grasses and the corn—it's oats this year, barley it was last year. There's a wee, windblown tree, and that's all. But every day and every week it looks a bit different—the flowers come and the corn grows so it seems silly to shift about. I just leave my painting table out here, and my easel and palette.[12]

Her photography in itself was something of a professional triumph, and gained a special section by Sara Stevenson in the book (*Joan Eardley*) by Fiona Pearson published by the Trustees of the National Galleries of Scotland to accompany an exhibition of her work at the National Gallery in November 2007–January 2008. Stevenson points out that in photographs details are captured that may elude notice when one views the scene *in vivo*, such as graffiti and background features, which can be included in any subsequent painting.

Another interesting device was the use of collage: she would add seeds and grasses from the actual landscapes she was painting—or, in Glasgow, newsprint and discarded sweet papers. She did not always spend the winters in Glasgow: she loved being in Catterline in stormy weather. In February 1958 she wrote:

> It [the snow] is piled up against the door and even out of drifts it is easily a foot deep. Anyway, in between blizzards it has been just so much what I wanted for my paint-ing that stupidly I imagined I could just rush out and in with my canvas. You know what a job it was setting up that canvas at the back of the house. Well, I've had it three or four times to do and the length of time that I actually had to paint was so brief—mostly about a quarter of an hour before the onset of the next blizzard. And I realised after I had given in that I hadn't helped my neck anything—it's awfulness to be such a crock. You really need to be tough for this game. [13]

Angus (living nearby) was on hand to anchor her easel to the ground. Audrey Walker also visited, and Lil Neilson, her friend from Hospitalfield (where Joan was guest tutor in summer 1961). Lil had trained at the Duncan of Jordanstone College of Art in Dundee. She had a travelling scholarship to France and Italy in 1961–2, and was then invited to Catterline by Joan.

Joan still suffered bouts of depression, but continued to find inspiration in wild weather:

> Then quite suddenly, in the middle of the afternoon, the wind veered to the east with no warning—a gale force wind. My painting and me were enveloped in snow—not from the sky but from the ground blown up—and everything I was looking at became blotted out by snow whirling everywhere from off the ground. That was the end of my day's work and, ever since, the wind has been bashing at this poor old house. Certainly the coldest and worst day of the year—a most exciting day, too, with every variation of colour—black sea, bright green striped sea, brown sea, yellow sea and no sea. Extraordinary strong cloud formations, too. [14]

These conditions gave rise to some stunning landscapes and snowscapes. The situ-ation could be grim when the village was snowed up, with mail and milk being delivered on sledges and the fishing boats wrecked by blizzards, without even going to sea. Joan's neck pains were getting worse. One wonders whether this was simply brought on by standing too long painting outside, or was actually metastases of the breast cancer, still to be diagnosed. But, like Kathleen Ferrier, Joan seemed desperate to carry on with her work until the very last minute. Her friend Audrey Walker wrote:

> …there were two Joans, though most people only knew one Joan… I always identify Joan with the sea… This was the Joan that I think everyone knew… There is the gentle sunlit sea one delights in, in the summer… But there is the magnificent winter sea, in all its indomitable grandeur and wild, turbulent and terrifying splendour. This was Joan too. But perhaps only three people knew this Joan really well. Two of them could not take it… but to me she was, quite simply, the winter sea to which and for which I would give my life… This Joan was to me godlike and her courage and tri-umph over the appalling conditions in which she painted these wonderful seas, when so

often she was suffering physical pain, is something to make an ordinary creature very humble. It was good to be there, having the house warm and a meal ready, and hot water, when she came home at dusk after a long day's work on the shore with this great white churning roaring sea and tremendous gale coming at her...[15]

Audrey remained married to Allan Walker, with whom she had a son, but it seems clear that she and Joan were in love. This extract shows that in certain respects the relationship was something like that between a conventional husband and wife, where the wife sees to the domestic duties while the husband goes out to work. One of Joan's letters to Audrey reads:

Love, this letter is all me me mee—how I really do hate letters for being like this—always my point of view. Your letters are never like this. But I haven't yet fathomed how you make them so unselfish.[16]

In a BBC interview in 1963, Joan said:

I very often find I'll take my paints to a certain place that has moved me and I'll begin to paint there and I've worn a kind of mark in the ground and I leave my paints there overnight and I seem to build up a sort of table and... a studio seems to have arrived outside and that seems to be how I work. Once I start in a place I find I don't want to move because I'm trying to do something and you are never really satisfied with what you're doing and the more you try the more you think of new ways of doing this particular subject so you just go on and on...[17]

No wonder she suffered from a stiff neck! In 1962 she painted some of her best work, for instance *A Field by the Sea: Summer*, now in the Royal Scottish Academy. At this point she probably knew that she did not have long to live. It was only in 1963 that she was elected a full member of the Royal Scottish Academy. By then she was seriously ill with breast cancer that had spread to the brain, causing double vision and severe headaches. She died on 16th August 1963.

After her death her work was reviewed and exhibited and praised as never before. More exhibitions were held in both Scotland and England, the most recent at the Scottish National Gallery of Modern Art (Edinburgh) in 2016–17.

It was also only after her death that the full extent of her relationships with women became more generally known. At the 2016–17 exhibition several personal letters were displayed, including a passionate one to Lil Neilson. In May 1963 Joan wrote to her from London, where she had gone to prepare for her solo exhibition at Roland, Browse and Delbanco:

My precious

That's another letter from you this morning—God what a difference that has made—because I'm missing you like hell too... my form of missing you is that I bloody can't get to sleep...I miss snuggling up against you...[18]

Lesbianism, though never illegal in the UK, unlike male homosexuality, was nevertheless not recognized as a legitimate partnership in Scotland until 2014, when the Marriage and Civil Partnership (Scotland) Act was passed. Only in 2017 was same-sex marriage allowed in the Episcopal Church of Scotland, but at the time of writing neither the Church of England nor the Church of Scotland permits or recognizes such ceremonies, or allows its clergy to bless same-sex couples who have undergone a civil marriage.

So it is understandable that Joan preferred to keep her partnerships private, and doing so must have been an added strain that she could have done without. This was in spite of the fact that her own aunt Sybil Morrison, who was a suffragette, feminist, and pacifist, did not choose to hide her lesbianism. Physically Joan was almost a caricature of the typical lesbian, with her corduroy trousers, short hair and generally masculine appearance. In about 1953 she wrote to her friend Francis Stephens, a stained glass artist:

> Well, being a lesbian in itself isn't a thing to worry me, but the trouble is that life hasn't worked out well at all, & I've reached a state of most unholy muddle, & my painting isn't going well either. Isn't everything inter-related?—and I just don't believe in masterpieces coming out of misery—it's nonsense: I know I paint best when I'm in a decently settled state.[19]

As for the characteristics of the typical 'cancer personality', Andreae notes her shyness. Josef Herman, a Polish Jewish artist escaping from the Nazis, wrote about his meeting with Joan:

> Though it was a warm day she wore a thick grey pullover, the kind usually worn by sailors or fishermen. The other girl was tiny, blonde and sweating. I shouted down to them to stop and wait for me. Then we all three carried the easel. In the studio the smaller girl was the more forthcoming. She introduced herself, and then her friend: Joan Eardley. Both were students at the Glasgow School of Art. Joan, though unbelievably shy—she could not utter a word without going red in the face—came frequently to my studio after this first meeting.[20]

Andreae thinks that Herman subsequently influenced Joan in the direction of social realism, even though he left Glasgow in 1943. All the same, her own vision was extraordinarily original, and her style has an unmistakable personal imprint. Andreae also notes that Joan was, 'by her own account not at all sociable'.[21]

So to sum up the issues that may have affected her emotional life and impinged on her immune system, we have first of all, in childhood, her father's suicide (though she did not know the details until much later), and the subsequent absence of a father figure. William Buchanan writes: 'Even as late as 1951 we read in a letter that she was troubled by her father's death: "A lonely and dark despondency is with me... when I can find work it will go."'[22]

Joan had a shy, inhibited personality, which found its most triumphant outlet in her artistic work. She managed to form intimate relationships, but the fact that she was quite obviously an almost stereotypical lesbian at a time when this was socially unacceptable added to her problems. This trait was illustrated quite early by her firm refusal to be a bridesmaid to her younger sister Pat, and her wearing of masculine-looking corduroy trousers at a time when women rarely wore trousers at all.

One of her closest relationships was that with Audrey Walker: from 1954 she wrote to her almost every day, though in later years it seems she was even closer to Lil Neilson (see the letter quoted earlier). In 1955 Joan wrote to Audrey:

> O dear dear you. I don't think phoning is a good thing. It makes you too near. I meant to make an arrangement to phone you again — but I suddenly felt — no — best just wire — and you will if you need me. Truly. Dear dear you… I wish you were here… One great big bursting feeling that means you — & means me & whole piles of things that haven't got words at all.
> O dear dear you — [23]

And later she wrote:

> Well dear one — goodnight — & take care of your wee self. Are you all right still? Do take care of yourself… Love to you — dear you —.
> Joan. [24]

But it seems that Joan was not taking care of her own self. She must have been ignoring the symptoms of breast cancer for a long while. By April 1963 she was seriously ill: she had just been elected as a Royal Scottish Academician, and in May her one-woman show opened at Roland, Browse and Delbanco in London. In London preparing for the exhibition she wrote to Lil Neilson:

> The doctor said my bosom had gone into a multiple cist [sic], so I guess I'd better see my own doctor when I get back. She gave me more little white pills, and seems hope-full [sic] enough. So I'm not bothering too much, but it would be interesting apart from anything else to see what the other side of the medical profession has to say. [25]

This implies that her London doctor was some kind of 'alternative' practitioner: we don't know what the 'little white pills' might have been. But obviously they did not help.

Joan was even invited to a Royal reception at Holyrood House in July: she was at the peak of her career. But she could not go: by now the cancer had spread to her brain, and she went for treatment to Aberdeen Royal Infirmary. She received radiotherapy, but it was too late: she was transferred to Killearn Hospital near Glasgow to be near her family, and died on 16th August, aged only 42. Her ashes were scattered on the beach at Catterline.

Select Bibliography

(All these books are lavishly illustrated with colour reproductions of Eardley's work)

Christopher Andreae: *Joan Eardley* (Lund Humphreys in association with the Scottish Gallery and the Portland Gallery, Farnham, Surrey, 2013)

William Buchanan: *Joan Eardley* (University Press, Edinburgh, 1976)

Patrick Elliott with Anne Galastro: *Joan Eardley: A Sense of Place* (National Galleries of Scotland, Edinburgh, 2016)

William Hardie: *Scottish Painting: 1837 to the Present* (Waverley Books, Glasgow, 2010)

Fiona Pearson: *Joan Eardley* (National Galleries of Scotland, Edinburgh, 2007)

Cordelia Oliver: *Joan Eardley, RSA* (Mainstream Publishing Company, Edinburgh, 1988)

Notes

1.   Oliver, p. 12.
2.   *ibid.*, p. 21.
3.   *ibid.*, p. 21.
4.   Andreae, p. 37.
5.   Oliver, p. 32.
6.   *ibid.*, p. 32.
7.   *ibid.*, p. 37.
8.   *ibid.*, p. 28.
9.   ibid., p. 52.
10.   *ibid.*, p. 64.
11.   *ibid.*, p. 73.
12.   *ibid.*, p. 76.
13.   *ibid.*, p. 84.
14.   *ibid.*, p. 85.
15.   Quoted in Andreae, p. 15.
16.   Quoted in Andreae, p. 24.
17.   Quoted in Pearson, pp. 55–6.
18.   Letter displayed at the 2016–17 Eardley exhibition *A Sense of Place at the National Gallery of Modern Art*, Edinburgh (private collection).
19.   Andreae, p. 161.
20.   Josef Herman: *Related Twilights, Notes from an Artist's Diary* (Robson Books, 1975), quoted in Andreae, p. 38.
21.   Andreae, p. 59.
22.   Buchanan, p. 82.
23.   Andreae, pp. 148–9.
24.   Andreae, p. 150.
25.   Elliott and Galastro, p. 68.

Susan Sontag

ALTHOUGH SUSAN HERSELF STRONGLY denied the theory of the 'cancer personality' in her perhaps best-known book, *Illness as Metaphor*, from her earliest days she seemed to illustrate precisely the cancer-prone life history that we have found common among our stories so far. She was born on 16th January 1933 as Susan Lee Rosenblatt, and 'felt alone at a very early age',[1] since her father, Jack Rosenblatt, was working in China as a fur merchant, and her mother Mildred re-joined him soon after her birth. Susan was left in the care of a nanny named Rose McNulty, living with Susan's paternal grandparents. The same pattern would recur when Susan's younger sister Judith was born in February 1936.

Though her parents were prosperous, Rosenblatt's business in Tientsin was not to last long. At the age of only 35, he died of pulmonary tuberculosis in the German American Hospital in Tientsin; Mildred postponed telling Susan for several months. After she was told, Susan (at the age of five) developed severe asthma, and Mildred moved the family first to Miami and then to Tucson, Arizona. This was a healthy place in which to live, surrounded by a beautiful desert landscape and well provided with hospitals for patients with respiratory ailments. But Susan's biographer Daniel Schreiber describes 'the life of an isolated and exceptionally gifted girl neglected by a widowed and emotionally unapproachable mother with a drinking problem'.[2]

Mildred found part-time work locally as a teacher, but she also disappeared on other occasions without telling Susan where she was going: the nanny took care of the girls. Later Susan suspected she might have had lovers. Susan started school in September 1939 just as the Second World War broke out, within a week she had been promoted to the third grade. She fibbed to her classmates that she had been born in China. Early on Susan was an avid reader, and was inspired by Eve Curie's biography of her mother Marie Curie.

America joined the war after the Japanese attack on Pearl Harbor on 7th December 1941, and from then on life became more difficult: some foods were rationed, there were power failures, and the local hospitals took in military casualties. Susan became conscious that her family originated in Lithuanian/Polish Jewry, and that the Jews were being persecuted as scapegoats by the German Reich. Soon she was writing a four-page magazine, which she planned to sell for five cents a copy. The writer in her demanded expression, and her subjects included recent battles. But she moved schools several times, and life must have been lonely and challenging. Her response was a burning desire to overcome and to succeed.

When Susan was 12 her mother married Captain Nathan Sontag, an air-force pilot who was recovering from war wounds in a Tucson sanatorium. He did not adopt Susan and Judith, but they did acquire his surname, which was less Jewish-sounding than their own, and in Susan's case attractively alliterative. She entered North Hollywood High School, and was soon editing the student newspaper *The Arcade*. But school lacked stimulus, and her intellectual impetus came from her extra-curricular reading fuelled by the nearby Pickwick Bookshop: at around 14 she was reading Franz Kafka and Thomas Mann. She was interested primarily in European culture, thinking of America as 'a colony of Europe'.[3] Her hunger for books was so great that she even stole them (to her later shame).

She made friends with Peter, who had also lost his father (a Hungarian Jew, murdered by the Gestapo). He and his French mother had escaped from France to Lisbon, and then America. Susan and Peter frequently saw movies together, holding hands. Their taste was distinctly intellectual. She also read highbrow periodicals such as the *Partisan Review*, and listened to chamber music, discussing with another friend, Merrill, the performances of the Busch and Budapest string quartets. Visual art too she studied. With Merrill she even visited Thomas Mann, whose novel *The Magic Mountain* had inspired her, but at the age of 14 she found meeting the author embarrassing. It resurfaced in her story 'Pilgrimage'.[4] This is one of several occasions when Susan used autobiographical material in her fiction.

Susan was still only 15 when she graduated from North Hollywood High School, and in early 1949, aged 16, she entered the University of California at Berkeley. Her Uncle Aaron agreed to pay for her accommodation. But her aim was to go to Chicago University, where she registered in September 1949. She shone in the entrance examination, and she was considered so brilliant that she was allowed to cover the four-year curriculum (in ancient history, philosophy and literature) in two years. While there she fell in love with a sociology lecturer, Philip Rieff, and within ten days they were married. Philip was a Lithuanian Jew, aged 28; Susan was only 17.

Susan wore jeans and sweaters, at that time something of a revolutionary outfit; she also kept her surname rather than taking Philip's. Already she was a feminist. When Philip obtained a teaching post at Brandeis University they moved to

Boston: their son David was born in Cambridge, Massachusetts, in September 1952, and Susan's former nanny Rose McNulty came along to care for the baby. Like her mother, Susan did not breast-feed. (This, of course, is a risk factor for breast cancer.) So Susan was able to continue her studies, and in 1953 enrolled as a graduate student at the University of Connecticut, but left after a year. She also started on the graduate programme in philosophy at Harvard, where she met several eminent intellectuals including Paul Tillich, Jacob Taubes, and Herbert Marcuse. She began to work as a teaching assistant in philosophy.

Here Susan continued with her feminist agenda, almost unconsciously, starting with her impatience with the tradition of men adjourning to a separate room to smoke cigars and discuss university politics after academic dinner parties. Once she decided to challenge the system and gate-crashed the male gathering. Philip Rieff became more and more embarrassed by this unconventional behaviour. But he accepted her help with research on his thesis *Freud: The Mind of the Moralist*, even though he was unwilling to acknowledge it. At the same time Susan was drifting away from Philip. In 1957 she gained an MA in philosophy from Harvard, and was recommended for a fellowship to go to Oxford University and work on a dissertation. Philip was offered a post at Stanford University. So their son David stayed with Philip's parents and his nanny while his own parents were both away in different continents.

At the age of 25, Susan arrived at St Anne's College, Oxford, to work on her dissertation. She wrote daily letters to Philip. But after only four months she decided that Oxford was not for her, and moved to Paris, living in Saint-Germain-des-Prés, a fashionable area full of galleries, bookshops, cafés and restaurants, with many American exiles. She loved Paris.

> *After work, or trying to write or paint, you come to a café looking for people you know. Preferably with someone, or at least with a definite rendez-vous... One should go to several cafés — average: four in an evening.*[5]

Her biographer writes:

> *Sontag is most interested in the 'role' of the artist, from which she hoped for relief from her insecure and problematic self. Through writing, she intended to reach the self she dared not fully embrace against the demands of her time, her family, and the academic life.*[6]

Since before her marriage Susan had been attracted to women as well as men. In Paris, with no family near by, she was free to make new liaisons. Her affair with Harriet Sohmers was particularly close. But Harriet had an ongoing heterosexual relationship with a Swedish painter, and the affair with Susan ended in disaster, when Susan came across Harriet's diary. Meanwhile Susan's relationship with Philip was cooling off, and she finally decided to divorce him. She told him when he met her at Boston airport in March 1959, and then picked up her son David and moved to New York. There she rented a simple apartment and lived in relative poverty, taking a temporary job as an editor on the journal *Commentary*: she refused alimony from her husband or child support for David. The divorce agreement even stipulated that she could not claim joint authorship of *Freud: The Mind of the Moralist*, a work into which she had put a good deal of effort.

In autumn 1959 Susan left her job at *Commentary* and took a part-time post at the City College of New York, and another at Sarah Lawrence College, which left her more time for her own work. Domestic duties were skimped, but David grew up in a stimulating intellectual atmosphere. Harriet Sohmers had also moved back to New York, and the two met up again, adding to their circle (Maria) Irene Fornés, a Cuban-American artist, and the writer Alfred Chester, all of whom had lived in Paris. The three women had affairs with each other, and Susan also had one with Alfred. Finally Susan and Irene became a serious item, and Irene moved into Susan's apartment in West End Avenue, where she stayed for two years. She features in Susan's diary *Reborn* as 'I'. Susan and her son David spent the summer of 1960 in Cuba with Irene. Both women found that their relationship stimulated their writing.

David was sent to visit his father in California and Pennsylvania as often as possible, but Susan did not want Philip to gain custody, which he now sought, on the grounds that Susan was an unfit mother owing to her lesbian relationships. The case went to trial, and although homosexuality was still illegal in New York, it was customary to grant custody of children to the mother, and Susan won the case.

Susan's life as a working mother must have been very stressful, but she continued to work on her first novel *The Benefactor*. She found a publisher for it in Farrar, Straus and Giroux, and in May 1961 signed a contract with the firm, securing a small advance. It was published in autumn 1963, with a stunning photograph of Susan on the back cover. Roger Straus was her mentor, and she stayed with FSG for the rest of her life. The book was not a huge success, but it facilitated her entry into the high culture circles she now penetrated and in which she blossomed.

In the first issue of the *New York Review of Books* in February 1963, Susan reviewed the collected essays of Simone Weil. Other contributors included Norman Mailer, Gore Vidal, W.H. Auden and Mary McCarthy. In 1964 various social movements took root, the New Left began to form, Martin Luther King Jr was awarded the Nobel Peace Prize (his 'I have a dream' speech was made in 1963), Congress passed the Civil Rights Act, and the Beatles visited the USA. In this year Susan Sontag also achieved fame. But there were so many demands on her time that her relationship with Irene suffered, and they finally split up.

Susan was becoming more and more involved with the world of writers, and her academic work was a casualty. However, her publisher helped with gaining her a post at Rutgers University for the academic year 1964–5, as writer in residence. She also received a fellowship from the Merrill Foundation for 1965. But she never completed her dissertation: instead, she became a freelance writer. She found that essays and criticism made more money than whole works, and began to focus on these, sometimes working through the night to beat deadlines. This was obviously not good for her health. At the same time she was a frantic film-goer, sometimes watching three or four films a day, particularly the avant-garde.

Her new preoccupation was 'Camp', which she spelt with a capital letter. The *Oxford English Dictionary* defined the term as early as 1909, as 'ostentatious, exaggerated, affected, theatrical, effeminate or homosexual'. Susan had difficulty getting her essay *Notes on 'Camp'* published, but she made it in 1964 in the *Partisan Review*. It was hugely influential, thrusting Susan into intellectual stardom from this point onwards, and appeared in her next book, a collection of essays: *Against Interpretation* (1966). Some found it rather bizarre, however, and I have to say that I was surprised to discover that:

> The late 17th century and early 18th century is the great period of Camp: Pope, Congreve, Walpole, etc., but not Swift; les précieux in France, the rococo churches of Munich, Pergolesi. Somewhat later, much of Mozart.[7]

What would Mozart have thought, I wonder?

But this essay and the subsequent volume certainly helped her career. She was awarded a year's Guggenheim Fellowship and the George Polk award for Cultural Criticism, and travelled widely, speaking at meetings all over Europe (her expenses paid). *Against Interpretation* still stimulates debate, and its breaking down of the barriers between 'high' art and popular culture was what made it particularly innovative and interesting. Susan also challenged the misogyny prevalent among her male colleagues.

However, her new celebrity was not acclaimed by everybody: she was dropped by the *New York Review of Books*. She was also accused of 'pseudo-intellectualism' by many viewers of the BBC TV programme *Monitor*, where she was interviewed by Jonathan Miller. She did not shy away from middlebrow magazines such as *Vogue*. She was seen as a role model by many feminists, and though Sontag's brand of intellectualism violated the British ideal of understatement and self-irony, that lack of modesty was not a problem in America, where people have always understood the need for self-promotion.[8]

Susan wanted to be famous, and achieved her ambition, with the help of her publisher and literary agents, who gained for her an international reputation. Her love life again became complicated; she had a long and difficult affair with Warren Beatty, and then another with Jasper John.

Susan's politics were as radical as her avant-garde writing and personal life. In line with many intellectuals she objected to the war between South Vietnam, supported by the USA, and Communist North Vietnam. She signed petitions against the war, and was even arrested with others who obstructed the entrance to a military recruitment centre in Lower Manhattan, though she was only held for two hours. However, much publicity resulted, and her essay 'What's happening in America', with its much-quoted indictment, 'The white race is the cancer of human history', again helped to raise her profile worldwide. This is included in the volume *Styles of Radical Will*.[9]

Susan then made a visit to Hanoi, which led to her account 'Trip to Hanoi', also included in *Styles of Radical Will*. In spite of her opposition to the war, she was by no means taken in by the propaganda of the Communist officials, and she saw real suffering among the people. But she accurately foresaw that North Vietnam would eventually win the war. Susan's second novel, *Death Kit*, was written 'in the shadow of the Vietnam war'.[11] However, the novel was not a success, and it took her 25 years to write another. The jacket for her early diaries *Reborn* (edited after her death by her son David Rieff) uses a photo of her smoking a cigarette and looking somewhat dark and moody: indicating a none too healthy lifestyle and a deep unhappiness.

In spite of her growing fame as a writer, Susan was somewhat conflicted in her thoughts and attitudes. Though remaining left wing, she began to distance herself increasingly from the New Left, and she suffered too from serious depression, writer's block, and financial worries. She decided to turn to film writing and directing. She moved again to Paris, and in 1967 was invited to be a member of the jury for the Venice Film Festival. She was now in a relationship with Carlotta del Pezzo, an Italian duchess. She then went to Sweden to work on her first film, *Duet for Cannibals*, writing the script in only three weeks. She began shooting in early 1969. The film was not a great success.

While Susan was travelling all over Europe, her publisher Roger Straus took care of things back home in New York, keeping an eye on David, now 17, who also began to travel widely on his own, sometimes crossing paths with his mother. Her own private life was now somewhat chaotic. A sad episode was the suicide of an old friend, Susan Taubes, which affected her deeply. She supported Susan's two children right up until her own death.

She then worked on another film, *Brother Carl*, and seems to have had another spell of depression, not helped by working in Stockholm in midwinter, with practically no sun. This film too was not a success. Susan now lived mainly in Paris from 1972 to 1975, returning only occasionally to New York. Her new romantic relationship was with Nicole Stéphane, an actress who after a serious accident changed to being a theatre producer. Once again Susan entered the Parisian circle of radical intellectuals. But her depression continued. She was also hard up, not being able to finance a somewhat extravagant lifestyle.

Eventually she started writing again, and her obituary of the novelist Paul Goodman, a co-founder of Gestalt therapy, won praise. She began to write short stories, several of which were autobiographical, and were published in the collection *I, etcetera* in 1978. It contained the story 'Project for a Trip to China'—a journey which took place in January 1973, adding to her tour of Communist countries. She also visited Israel, which provided material for her next film, *Promised Lands*, achieving success at the Chicago film festival. She wrote furiously; her publisher found her a Rockefeller Fellowship and a Guggenheim Fellowship, so she was financially secure for a good while.

Susan now embarked on a new project, a book containing six essays, finally published as *On Photography* (1977). While working on this she attended her doctor for a routine check-up and was found to have advanced breast cancer (Stage 4, with several metastases). She was only 42, and tumours are known to grow faster in younger women.

Like many other women at the time she felt patronized by the way doctors talked to her. The prognosis was very poor: there was only a 10 per cent chance of surviving two years. She determined to read all she could in medical journals about treatment. She underwent a radical mastectomy, followed by two and a half years of high-dose chemotherapy. She had no medical insurance, and somehow had to raise the substantial sum required to cover her treatment, during which she was unable to work. So a group of friends set up a fund for her medical expenses, which they largely covered.

During Susan's therapy she went out every evening she could possibly manage physically, to the theatre, cinema, opera, or meals with friends. (Her son David, and his girlfriend Sigrid Nunez, were living with her at the time.) She finished her book *On Photography* (1977) and started *Illness as Metaphor* (1978), in which she attacked the thesis propounded by Lawrence LeShan which has provided the theme for this book: that emotional history has a part to play in the causation of cancer. In those days, as I know from personal experience in the UK, the diagnosis of cancer was often kept from the patient, and only divulged to relatives: there was something shameful about even the word 'cancer'. People were frightened, seeing it as a death sentence. The taboo infuriated Susan, who was also furious with LeShan's thesis. But obviously she was half persuaded by it none the less.

She told several interviewers that, after her initial diagnosis, she asked herself whether she had lived her life wrongly and the breast cancer was somehow the result of the depression she had experienced in Paris.[11]

Susan was acutely aware of the use of the word 'cancer' as denoting catastrophe, even quoting her own pronouncement: 'The white race is the cancer of human history'. The book *Illness as Metaphor* was an immediate success, with both doctors and patients worldwide. She also welcomed contact with other cancer patients, becoming something of a one-woman support group. But in spite of her wide knowledge and research, in order to continue both her social life and her writing, for which she struggled to meet deadlines, she resorted to amphetamines to get by. Surely this was unwise while she was still on chemotherapy.

Her appearance also changed. Her hair fell out during her chemotherapy, and grew back white. She decided to dye it black (hair dye has known toxicities), but left one fashionable streak still white, which served as a distinctive signature. When she resumed work she was productive as never before, publishing volumes of essays and short stories. She had been dividing her time between Paris (seeing Nicole Stéphane) and New York, but she now slowly separated from Nicole, moving back to New York full time. Her reputation in Europe, and particularly in Germany, increased rapidly, and in 2003 she was awarded the Peace Prize of the German Book Trade.

Susan wrote as a freelance, and did not wish to accept an academic post, even though this meant continuing financial insecurity. However, she had a mission: 'to bring together art, literature, film, and politics and communicate their interrelatedness to her readers'.[12] Susan's son David was now working as an editor with her publishers, Farrar, Straus and Giroux.

Susan's left-wing sympathies were dealt a huge blow by contact with the writers exiled from their European homelands by Communist régimes, and her own visit to Poland in 1980. Her change of viewpoint also owed something to Joseph Brodsky, who was banished from the Soviet Union in 1972, and after a brief relationship with Susan proposed marriage. They did not marry, but continued to be friends and saw each other often. Brodsky certainly influenced Susan's thinking, and she became an enthusiastic reader of classical Russian fiction. She still wanted to write fiction, but found this difficult. She acknowledged: 'Essay writing is part of an addiction that I'm trying to kick. My last essay is like my last cigarette.'[13] (In spite of her cancer she could not give up smoking.)

Her original sympathies with Communism were now reversed. As always she expressed her feelings in outright terms: she considered Communism to be 'Fascism with a Human Face'.[14] This volte-face created indignation among New York intellectual circles. But Susan continued to thrive on her publicity, even if adverse. She became somewhat narcissistic, and lost some friends while gaining others. But although her creative fire was certainly not foiled, it perhaps became somewhat diffuse, covering a wide range of subject matter. She had to keep writing in order to pay her bills. She had no television set, but saw many plays, films and operas, and read many books, often reviewing them for *Vanity Fair*. She also made a film about Venice, resulting in a new relationship with the leading actor, Lucinda Childs.

A contemporary theme was AIDS, with its parallels with cancer: some of her close friends died from it. Her experience here resulted in her book *Aids and its Metaphors* (1989). She also promoted other writers, and became President of the American PEN (a worldwide association of writers, founded in London in 1921 to promote friendship and intellectual co-operation among writers). She served from 1987 to 1989. Her work for PEN involved organizing public readings of the works of imprisoned writers, as well as protests on their behalf. She ruffled feathers, but also achieved much.

While still PEN president in February 1989 Susan campaigned for Salman Rushdie, whose book *The Satanic Verses* had led the Ayatollah of Iran to issue a fatwa ordering Muslims to kill him. Rushdie was a friend of Susan's, and she called for a public statement from PEN. Although Britain had ended diplomatic ties to Iran, the U.S. government had not followed suit, in spite of Susan's advocacy. At this point in her life her admirable campaigning for good causes was often spoilt by her tendency to exaggeration and to lash out at interviewers. 'It was a time when Susan Sontag's passionate defence of her life as an independent intellectual often shaded into exaggerated caricature and even self-glorification.'[15]

In 1988 the photographer Annie Leibovitz had taken her photo for the dust jacket of a new edition of *Illness as Metaphor*. She was 39, Susan now 55. They became lovers, though unacknowledged publicly, in spite of urging by friends to 'come out'. Susan's finances were still precarious. A fire in her New York flat did not help. But her situation improved when Andrew Wylie became her literary agent, and worked wonders, especially with foreign publication of her books.

Susan began work on *The Volcano Lover*, based on the story of Emma Hamilton and Horatio Nelson. The book was published in autumn 1992 and was very well reviewed. It seemed that at last Susan had found her true voice. But having achieved success as a novelist, Susan now turned to the theatre, writing a play about Alice James, the sister of Henry James, a feminist icon, who died of breast cancer aged 45 in 1892. Her story had obvious parallels with Susan's own. The title was *Alice in Bed*. It was premiered in Bonn in 1991, but not performed in New York until 2000. It was not well received.

However, a real success was achieved with her brave production of Beckett's *Waiting for Godot* in Sarajevo, then at the centre of the civil war in Bosnia. This was a hugely important experience for her. She first visited Sarajevo in 1993 to see her son David, who was working there as a journalist, and this inspired her to return and produce the play, starting rehearsals in July 1993. She found immense practical difficulties, such as lack of food and electricity (the stage was lit with candles). She cut the play to one act, in view of the problems people had getting home safely afterwards. *Waiting for Godot* aptly symbolized the hazardous wait the people were enduring while longing for rescue from the siege, which was only lifted two years later. The play attracted international interest, and journalists flocked to the city to review the production. Some accused Susan of attention seeking, which hurt her deeply, but she earned the esteem and gratitude of the Bosnians, who granted her honorary citizenship and other honours.

Susan's personality sometimes got the better of her. While compelled to support good causes, and admired for it, she often irritated even her supporters with her narcissistic and unpredictable behaviour, once walking out of a PEN banquet because the person next to her did not recognize her. Although Susan it seemed could not give up smoking, she improved her diet somewhat after her breast cancer. But in

July 1998, aged 65, on a check-up she was found to have uterine sarcoma. She had a hysterectomy followed by chemotherapy and radiotherapy, and was in considerable pain for some time. She was visited daily while in the Mount Sinai Hospital in New York by Annie Leibovitz, and by her agent Andrew Wylie. The chemotherapy caused neuropathy in her feet, and she had to learn to walk again, but she was determined to continue writing, and with Annie Leibovitz produced the volume *Women*, a collection of photographs of women in many different roles that was something of a feminist manifesto.

She now allowed her hair to grow back white, and wore it cropped short. Once again, her creative fire was not foiled, and she was capable of staying up all night to beat a deadline. Remarkably, she began to have piano lessons: this she had been denied as a child by her mother. A new historical novel, *In America*, was published but was not a huge success, in spite of Susan's noble efforts at publicizing it by means of a speaking tour all over America. She was also accused of plagiarism. However, the book did receive a National Book Award, earning her $10,000.

Susan was now nearly 70 but was as active as ever, visiting Europe and particularly Paris, where Annie now had a flat on the Quai des Grands Augustins. Her philanthropic instincts were still alive, and her campaigning was crucial in the successful project to free the Chinese poet Bei Ling, who was arrested on a visit to China in 2000. She continued to write, but erratically:

> *I don't feel the need to write every day or even every week. But when I get started on something I just sit for 18 hours and suddenly realize that I have to pee. Many days I start in the morning and suddenly it's dark and I haven't gotten up. It's very bad for the knees.*[16]

And of course for the immune system. It seems remarkable that Susan, with her high intelligence and her overwhelming desire to keep writing, took so little care of her own health.

At this point Carl Rollyson and Lisa Paddock published their unauthorized and unsympathetic biography, despite Susan's trying to prevent it. In fact it did little damage to her reputation, and she continued to receive literary prizes: she also continued her fearless campaigning. She shot to notoriety with the attack on New York on 11th September 2001, when she happened to be not at home but in Berlin. She stepped way out of line with most commentators, saying:

> *Where is the acknowledgement that this was not a 'cowardly' attack on 'civilization' or 'humanity' or 'the free world' but an attack on the world's self-proclaimed superpower, undertaken as a consequence of specific American alliances and actions?*[17]

This even though she later declared herself an 'appalled, sad American and New Yorker'.[18]

Perhaps being away from home gave her a sense of perspective, and a view of American policy under Bush that was more objective than it might have been had she been at home and heard the noise of the attack. But it did not gain her any friends, and she even had death threats. On her return home she visited the site of the bombing, which somewhat changed her view of the event. But her political stance of criticizing the Bush administration in America did not abate, and she was a loud critic of the Iraq war. *Regarding the Pain of Others*, published in March 2003, coinciding with the start of the war, sums up her thoughts on the atrocities of warfare.

Whom do we think we have the right to blame? The children of Hiroshima and Nagasaki were no less innocent than the young African American men (and a few women) who were butchered and hanged from trees in small town America. More than one hundred thousand civilians, three fourths of them women, were massacred in the RAF firebombing of Dresden on the night of February 13 1945, seventy-two thousand civilians were incinerated in seconds by the American bomb dropped on Hiroshima. The roll call could be much longer. Again, Whom do we wish to blame?[19]

In perhaps a moment of foresight in 2002, Susan signed a contract to sell her considerable library and other papers to the University of California for $1.1 million. Susan was awarded the prestigious Peace Prize of the German Book Trade in October 2003, and soon afterwards the Prince of Asturias Award for literature in Oviedo, Spain. She lectured in London and South Africa, and wrote a number of forewords for republication of modern classics (for example, Pasternak, Rilke). Her sense of social responsibility dominated her last years, and the volume of essays *At the Same Time*, which was not published until after her death.

In the meantime, in early 2004 she had to cope with a third bout of cancer, this time myelodysplastic syndrome, leading to acute leukaemia, for which the cause was most probably the radiotherapy undergone for her breast cancer in 1976. This led to panic attacks. Susan still had many things she wanted to achieve, so instead of palliative care she opted for a bone marrow transplant, which gave only a faint chance of survival. In fact the transplant was not a success, resulting in acute pain, and Susan finally died on 28th December 2004, in the Memorial Sloan-Kettering Hospital in New York, surrounded by friends and her son David.

In conclusion, even though Susan strongly denied the thesis of the link between life events, depression and cancer proposed in this book, she herself illustrates it perfectly: an emotionally starved childhood, difficult relationships in adult life, with an inability to publicly acknowledge her lesbian affairs, and resulting bouts of depression. However, her creative fire was not foiled, and enabled her to defy her extremely gloomy prognosis with Stage 4 cancer at the age of 42, and to produce some of her best work thereafter. Even if some of it was highly controversial, she inspired others, and is still something of a feminist icon.

Select Bibliography

Biographical material

Benjamin Moser: *Sontag: Her Life* (Allen Lane, 2019) was brought to my attention only after the book had been sent to the publisher, and when owing to Coronavirus restrictions it was not possible to see a copy. *HG*

Sigrid Nunez: *Sempre Susan: a memoir of Susan Sontag* (Riverhead Books, Penguin Group, New York, 2011)

David Rieff: *Swimming in a Sea of Death: a son's memoir* (Simon & Schuster, New York, 2008; Granta Books, London, 2008, paperback 2009)

Carl Rollyson and Lisa Paddock: *Susan Sontag: The Making of an Icon* (W.W. Norton & Co. Inc., New York, 2000)

Daniel Schreiber: *Susan Sontag: a biography*, translated from the German by David Dollenmayer (Northwestern University Press, Evanston, Illinois, 2014)

Susan Sontag: *Reborn: Early diaries 1947–1963*, edited by David Rieff (Farrar, Straus and Giroux, New York, 2008; Hamish Hamilton, London, 2009)

Susan Sontag: *As Consciousness is Harnessed to Flesh: Diaries 1964–1980*, edited by David Rieff (Farrar, Straus and Giroux, New York, 2012; Hamish Hamilton, London, 2012; Penguin, London, 2013)

Fiction by Susan Sontag

I, Etcetera (Victor Gollancz, London, 1979)
Death Kit (Penguin Modern Classics, London, 2009)
Stories, ed. Benjamin Taylor (Penguin, London, 2017)
The Volcano Lover: a romance (Farrar, Straus and Giroux, New York, 1992, Penguin Modern Classics, London, 2009)

Essays by Susan Sontag

Against Interpretation and other essays (first published 1961; Penguin Classics, London, 2009)
Illness as Metaphor, and *Aids and its Metaphors*, in one volume (Penguin Books, London, 1991)
Where the Stress Falls (Farrar, Straus and Giroux, New York, 2001; Penguin Classics, London, 2009)

Regarding the Pain of Others (Farrar, Straus and Giroux, New York, 1992; Hamish Hamilton, London, 2003; Penguin, London, 2004)
At the Same Time, ed. Paolo Dilonardo and Anne Jump (Farrar, Straus and Giroux, New York, 2007; Penguin, London, 2008)

Notes

1. Rollyson and Paddock, p. 4.
2. Schreiber, p. 4.
3. *ibid.*, p. 21.
4. Sontag, *Stories*, pp. 3–29.
5. Sontag, *Reborn*, p. 160.
6. Schreiber, p. 46.
7. Sontag, *Against Interpretation*, p. 280.
8. Schreiber, p. 93.
9. Quoted in Schreiber, p. 104, from Sontag, *Styles of Radical Will* (Farrar, Straus and Giroux, New York, 1969, p. 203).
10. Quoted in Schreiber, p. 109, from Sontag, ibid., p. 194.
11. Schreiber, p. 147.
13. *ibid.*, p. 162.
14. *ibid.*, p. 164.
15. *ibid.*, p. 179.
16. *ibid.*, p. 220.
17. *ibid.*, p. 227.
18. *ibid.*, p. 228.
19. Sontag, *Regarding the Pain of Others* (Penguin edn), p. 83.

Audre Lorde

A tribute to Audre Lorde by Jackie Kay in *The Guardian* of 13th October 2008 ran:

> Poet, mother, lesbian, feminist, African-American — Audrey Lorde believed in naming the names. She wrote with ground-breaking eloquence about the complexities of identity, and was convinced that silence was the greatest enemy.[1]

She was born on 18th February 1934 in New York, and given the name Audrey Geraldine Lorde, though at the age of four she insisted on changing 'Audrey' to 'Audre', so making two words symmetrically ending in 'e'.

Her parents were both from the Caribbean, her mother Linda from

the small island of Carriacou and her father Byron from Barbados. Her mother was lighter-skinned than her father; she herself was the darkest of the three children: she had two older sisters, Helen and Phyllis. Her early childhood was problematic: her eyesight was extremely poor, and it was only at the age of four that she was equipped with spectacles. Even then, her parents disapproved of sunglasses, and bright light caused her great discomfort in summer. Her relationship with her parents was difficult and distant: the first indication that her emotional life was to be fraught. She started writing poetry at an early age. A positive influence from her mother was the importance to her of green things, especially trees and water in parks. But:

> Being black and foreign and female in New York city in the twenties and thirties was not simple, particularly when she was quite light enough to pass for white but her children weren't.[2]

Corporal punishment was routine in the household. At the age of five, in September 1939, Audre started at the Catholic school attended by her older sisters. She wrote in *Zami*:

> Even though I had two older sisters, I grew up feeling like an only child, since they were quite close to each other in age, and quite far away from me... The fact that I was clothed, sheltered and fed better than many other children in Harlem in those Depression years was not a fact that impressed itself too often upon my child's consciousness...[3]

By the time the Second World War arrived in the USA, with the Japanese attack on Pearl Harbor in 1941, Audre was reading the news, and listening to the radio, 'captivated and frightened by the high drama'.[4] But at school:

> The Sisters of Charity were downright hostile. Their racism was unadorned, unexcused, and particularly painful because I was unprepared for it. I got no help at home. The children in my class made fun of my braids, so Sister Victoria, the Principal, sent a note home to my mother asking her to comb my hair with more 'becoming' fashion, since I was too old, she said, to wear 'pigtails'.[5]

Though not enshrined in law, as it was in the southern States, racism was rife. On one occasion Audre's family stopped at a soda fountain for an ice cream. They were refused service on the premises, only offered ice cream to take away. The family walked away outraged, without their ice cream.

Audre remembered another event on a subway train in New York, when she was with her mother bringing home the Christmas shopping, and she sat down next to a woman who drew her coat closer to herself, as if to avoid contact with something unpleasant.

> No word has been spoken. I'm afraid to say anything to my mother because I don't know what I've done. I look at that side of my snowpants, secretly. Is there something on them? Something's going on here I do not understand, but I will never forget it. Her eyes. The flared nostrils. The hate.[6]

In high school Audre reported that: 'my real sisters were strangers; my teachers were racists, and my friends were that color I was never supposed to trust.'[7] It was not helpful either that she had a late menstruation, at the age of 14½. A session between her mother and a school counsellor was not a success.

> Depression was triggered by the suicide of a warm friend, Genevieve Johnson. Gennie had been the first person in my life that I was conscious of loving. And she had died. Loving hurt too much. My mother had turned into a demon intent on destroying me. You loved people and you came to depend on their being there. But people died or changed or went away and it hurt too much. The only way to avoid that pain was not to love anyone, and not to let anyone get too close or too important.[8]

When she left high school she also left home: a brief affair with Gerry Levine was the main reason. She had met him at a Labor Youth League party. Her father would not let him into the house because he was white. She hoped she would get used to sex with Gerry. But Gerry himself broke it up after a few months.

In autumn 1951 Audre signed up with Hunter College for a degree course, but in autumn 1952 she abandoned it and moved to Stanford, Connecticut, to find work. Her father Byron died early in 1953. Audre went to the funeral, staying several days in New York, and then returned to Connecticut, where she found a job at Keystone Electronics: here she was constantly exposed to carbon tetrachloride, which can cause cancer of the liver and kidney. This may have contributed to Audre's cancer. She was also exposed to X-ray machines. She was finally fired.

In 1954–5, at the age of 20, Audre spent a year in Mexico, where she had a lesbian relationship with Eudora Garrett, who had had a mastectomy but refused to wear a prosthesis. Audre then returned to New York, taking various odd jobs before studying for a degree in literature and philosophy, which she achieved at Hunter College in 1959, and then a master's degree in library science from Columbia in 1961.

When she started again at Hunter College in 1955, Audre was working 48 hours a week at the hospital as a medical receptionist, and 15 hours more at the college. And then, 'Just before Christmas, I got a job through college, working afternoons for a doctor. That provided me with money to get my typewriter out of hock, and a little more time to be depressed.'[9]

In late 1957, now 24, Audre went into psychotherapy with Clement Staff: she was troubled by nightmares. To be black, female, and gay, which she now began to acknowledge, were all difficult issues. But after a number of sessions with Clement, he died, which came as a shock to Audre. In the throes of an almost suicidal depression, Audre found another therapist, Dr Rosenbloom, who treated her free of charge because she was a student.[10] She had several lesbian attachments, and had become part of a group of young intellectuals, but she was the only black woman among them. After an evening with one of her friends (or lovers) she would drink coffee or take amphetamines to keep going. Again, this was not a good idea from the cancer point of view.

Audre felt compelled to fight on behalf of black women, first pointing out that they were the poorest paid in America (which she always spelt with a lower case A, whereas Black was always spelt with a capital B). Audre's direction was consistently towards the ironing out of any kind of discrimination against black women:

For it is through the coming together of self-actualised individuals, female and male, that any real advances can be made. The old sexual power relationships based on a dominant/subordinate relationship between unequals have not served us as a people, nor as individuals.[11]

During this time she worked as a librarian in Mount Vernon, New York. She became involved with Edwin Rollins, a white Jewish lawyer.

As their courtship evolved, they came to understand that neither was interested in a conventional marriage, though both believed in the conventions of marriage and that they could raise children in a new kind of family... What would it mean to marry a white man in the heat of the civil rights movement and the black revolution? What would it mean about her own blackness? What would it really mean to have interracial children?[12]

However, she did marry Edwin, on 31st March 1962, in St Mary's Church on 126th Street. They had two children, Elizabeth and Jonathan. Audre wanted Ed to accompany her to birthing classes, and be with her at the births; she then breast-fed them both. In the case of her firstborn, Elizabeth (Beth), she weaned her and left her with her sister Phyllis so as to go with Ed to the March on Washington in 1963, where Martin Luther King, Jr, gave his 'I Have a Dream' speech. Audre and Ed listened to King's speech on the way home in the car.

Ed had no salaried job at the time, though he was doing freelance work, and he became depressed. Their apartment caught fire (owing to Ed's discarded cigarette end) while they were away from home briefly, and they moved several times before settling down at 626 Riverside Drive, in 1966. Audre was now appointed head librarian at Town School Library, in New York City, staying till 1968.

Her relationship with Ed was complicated; they were both bisexual, and both had affairs. They shared the childcare, but Audre always wanted to be dominant in the marriage. She brought her lesbian partners home, but Ed didn't do the same — he would go off on excursions without telling her where he was going.

As Ed was not earning much, Audre worked in the library at night, having to ignore Jonathan's cries at her leaving him. She overdid it and became ill with flu. But then she was offered a 'poet in residence' assignment at Tougaloo, a black college in Mississippi. She accepted the invitation, arriving early in February 1968, since Ed volunteered to look after the children in her absence. During her time there she was expected to work on her own poetry, and also give public readings. She avowed her white husband, and became involved in a series of interesting discussions with students. But in fact the marriage was going nowhere.

While at Tougaloo she met Frances Clayton, who was associate professor of psychology at Brown University, and had rejected several marriage proposals before she met Audre. The two fell in love, and this finally led to Audre's divorce from Ed in 1970. Her romantic life now centred on Frances, who remained her lesbian partner until 1989.

Audre was back in New York at the Tougaloo concert in Carnegie Hall on 4th April 1968 when Martin Luther King, Jr, was killed in Memphis, Tennessee. The black community was devastated, and there were nationwide riots. After a disappointing course teaching at Herbert Lehman College, in 1968–70, when she had few black students, Audre started teaching at the John Jay College of Criminal Justice in Manhattan. She embarked on a course that she called 'Race and the Urban Situation'. Her course was well attended, with a mix of black and white police and black and white students. At the time, Ed had left her, but Frances had not moved in, so she was lonely and depressed.

But by 1971 Audre and Frances had decided to live together, and Frances had to move from Rhode Island to New York, since the terms of Audre's divorce said that she and the children had to stay in New York State. The family moved to Staten Island, where they bought a property at 207 St Paul's Avenue. There the whole family was often the target of prejudice; but Frances liked the fresh air, and the children got used to their third floor apartment.

Ed Rollins took the children out at weekends, but became dilatory with child support payments. Finally Audre took him to court, and won. Frances took a large part in looking after the children, and also fulfilled to some extent Audre's desire for a mother figure: her earlier lesbian attachments had all been with younger women (Frances was born in 1926). But Audre could not resist occasional affairs with other women, which Frances resented.

At this point Audre was publishing her third book of poems, *From a Land Where Other People Live*, but the publisher wanted her to remove one of the poems, 'Love Poem', which was obviously lesbian. She did, and remained on good terms with the publisher, Dudley Randall, of Broadside Press. The book was nominated for the 1974 National Book Award for poetry.

In April 1973 Audre went to Barbados in search of information about her father. She chose Easter week for this expedition, and she found out that Frederick Byron Lorde was probably born in 1898; he was younger than her mother, though she denied this. Audre enjoyed learning about her father's culture, even though she could not fill in all the gaps in his story. It was during 1973 that Audre publicly came out as a lesbian, when she was reading her 'Love Poem' at a gathering of women. It was then published in the February 1974 issue of *Ms*. It also figured in a later volume published by her original publisher.

Another foreign trip was the whole family's five-week visit to West Africa, on 13th July 1974: first to Lorne, the capital of Togo, and then to Ghana. Audre herself really enjoyed the trip, finding links with her ancestors; not so much Frances and the children (aged 10 and 11), who still felt American, and had various issues throughout: the food was too spicy, they couldn't drink the water, they were affected by the heat. Audre felt offended when waiters deferred to Frances, and gave her the bill. But in Dahomey she found a spiritual home, and adopted the local goddess, Seboulisa, as her own.

On her return to America again Audre suffered from depression: she wondered whether this was due to her feelings about Jonathan, isolated in an all-female family. She employed Robert Turner, a psychiatric social worker (who was black), to take him out on Saturdays. This went well until Jonathan discovered he was being paid to spend time with him, and refused to see him again. That year (1975) she did many poetry readings, some unpaid, but she signed up with a new agent, Charlotte Sheedy, who made sure she was paid. In September 1976 Audre went to a conference in Uzbekistan (then part of the USSR), which brought together writers from oppressed groups, mainly in Africa and Asia. Frances looked after the children when Audre went on extramural trips.

By now, aged 42, 'Lorde had a solid reputation as a feminist lesbian literary figure.'[13] Her next visit abroad was to Lagos, Nigeria, for the Second World Black and African Festival of Arts and Culture, in January/February 1977. The Nigerians spent a fortune on a new National Theatre for the occasion, together with various other buildings, and there was a particularly large contingent of delegates from the USA, who were visibly moved by their experience of the country from which their ancestors had come as slaves. The aims of the organization were:

To ensure the resurgence and propagation of the cultures, cultural values, and civilisations of the African diaspora; to promote black and African visual artists, performers and writers, facilitating for them a global audience and greater access to worldwide outlets; to encourage, through cultural production, a return to Africa by those uprooted to other continents; and to promote interactive and international understanding.[14]

On 1st February Audre left for home. A feminist quarterly, *Chrysalis*, was launched in Los Angeles in February 1977, and Audre agreed to be its poetry editor; it accepted lesbian material, and she liked the general tone. Audre remained poetry editor for two years, during which she was able to repay certain friends who had helped her by publishing their work, among them Diane di Parma, Adrienne Rich, and Pat Parker, the first black lesbian she had known. Audre now began to open her readings with the information that she was 'Black, lesbian, feminist, mother, poet warrior'.

In November 1977 Audre found a lump in her breast, which was a huge shock. It was removed and found to be benign, but the fear of cancer underlay everything she did from that time. Audre's next trip, in March 1978, was with Frances to Grenada, where her mother grew up, though she was actually born on the nearby small island of Carriacou. She was anxious to fill in the gaps in her mother's story, as she had done for her father in Barbados. While there she felt sympathy (at last) with Mrs Lorde. In 1978 she published *The Black Unicorn*, a collection of 67 poems. It celebrated her two visits to West Africa, in 1974 and 1977. In 'A Litany for Survival' she wrote:

And when the sun rises we are afraid
it might not remain
when the sun sets we are afraid
it might not rise in the morning
when our stomachs are full we are afraid
of indigestion
when our stomachs are empty we are afraid
we may never eat again
when we are loved we are afraid
love will vanish...[16]

Mental health was an important issue for her. In 'Eulogy for Alvin Frost' she wrote: 'The only way to avoid that pain was not to love anyone, and not to let anyone get too close or too important.'[19]

I am tired of holy deaths...
where mental health is the ability
to repress
knowledge of the world's cruelty[17]

Audre now found a large lump in her right breast, and after a biopsy that confirmed it was malignant, she had a mastectomy in the Memorial Sloan Kettering Cancer Center on 22nd September 1978. She remembered Eudora Garrett, the woman she had known in Mexico in 1954. She explored alternative treatments, and did not want chemotherapy or radiotherapy, as she suspected they were toxic. But she made significant changes to her diet, advised by Dr Alice Francis, a chiropractor, who suggested less red meat and more vegetables. Like Eudora, she refused to wear a prosthesis.

She spoke about her experience on 28th December 1978 at a meeting in Chicago, where the subject was: 'The Transformation of Silence with Language and Action'. She had come face to face with death, she told her audience, 'and now she knew there were no silences worth keeping.'[15]

Her next conference was one honouring the work of Simone de Beauvoir: 'The Second Sex — Thirty Years Later: A Commemorative Conference on Feminist Theory', held at New York University in Manhattan on 27–29 September 1979. At this conference Audre stood out as an angry voice; she noticed that her chief concerns, about race, sexuality, class, and age, were not addressed by the main panel, and she publicly castigated her colleagues for this at the Saturday afternoon panel on 'The Personal and the Political'.

But things were moving on. On Sunday 14th October 1979 there was the first national march on Washington for Lesbian and Gay Rights. Two days earlier, the first National Third World Gay and Lesbian Conference took place in Harrambee House Hotel in the District of Columbia. Audre gave the keynote address: 'When Will the Ignorance End?' In it she said: 'And for me, it was only the consciousness, the vision, of a community somewhere, someday, it was only my vision of the existence and possibility of what is, in fact, here tonight, that helped to keep me sane.'[18] This was a significant speech, to a huge audience. She also found common cause with gay men, which she had not done before.

Audre was now through with *Chrysalis*, but was increasingly away from her family to go to various meetings. In November 1979 she left Jonathan and Beth, now 15 and 16, in the care of Frances, to go to the MacDowell Colony in Peterborough, New Hampshire, for a month. At MacDowell, artists and writers occupy one-room cabins, bereft of television or even telephone, with space to focus on their work. Breakfast and dinner are taken together, but lunch is delivered to the cabin. Audre focused on her new book *Zami*, but she experienced another episode of depression.

She also now wrote about cancer, very eloquently. In her introduction to *The Audre Lorde Compendium*, which includes *The Cancer Journals*, Alice Walker wrote:
> *What I love about Audre Lorde is her political and emotional honesty, her passion for living life as herself, her understanding of what a privilege and joy this is... I love her stare back into the eyes of death, as cancer stalked her, and finally dragged her down.*[19]

In the book, Audre wrote:

June 20 1980

I do not forget cancer for very long, ever. That keeps me around and on my toes, but also with a slight background noise of fear. Carl Simonton's book Getting Well Again has been really helpful to me… The visualisations and deep relaxing techniques that I learned from it help make me a less anxious person…[20]

Audre was visited in hospital by a Reach to Recovery volunteer, but found her not sympathetic to her real concerns. She also felt rejected by the kind nurse, who tried to persuade her to wear a prosthesis: this felt insulting. Audre was scathing about the American Cancer Society, which at the time was the largest non-religious charity in the world, making the point that there was no profit in the prevention of cancer, only in its treatment. She argued that it had not publicized the links between animal fat, from animals given artificial hormones, and breast cancer: 'What would happen if an army of one-breasted women descended upon Congress and demanded that the use of carcinogenic fat-stored hormones in beef is outlawed?'[21] She also said: 'We owe ourselves the protection of all the information about the treatment of cancer and its causes, as well as about the recent findings concerning immunology, nutrition, environment, and stress.'[23]

After Audre's mastectomy, she needed to talk to others who had had the same experience, and accepted invitations to speak at conferences all over the world, with an overwhelming response. In *Sister Outsider*, she asked: 'how do you deal with the fact that the women who clean your houses and tend your children while you attend conferences on feminist theory are, for the most part, poor women and women of color?'[24] She felt 'anxious for more living': 'Breast cancer, with its mortal awareness and the amputation which it entails, can still be a gateway, however cruelly won, into the tapping and expansion of my own power and knowing.'[22]

In April 1981 Audre responded to an invitation from the English department at Hunter saying that she would teach on the subject: 'American Fiction and Poetry since World War II', which she continued for the next five years.

Audre attended the National Women's Studies Association (NWSA) Convention in June, with the theme 'Women Respond to Racism'. She was giving the second keynote address, after Adrienne Rich (who was white, and made the point that white women too were obedient to and complicit in their own oppression). Her address had the title 'The Uses of Anger', emphasizing particularly her anger at white feminist academics, attacking the NWSA for refusing to waive the registration fee for poor women (which disproportionately affected women of colour). Her next challenge was an invitation from Dagmar Schultz, who had been at the NWSA meeting, to teach at the John F. Kennedy Institute for North American Studies at the Free University in Berlin, in the summer of 1983. Dagmar also introduced Audre to various complementary treatments available in Germany but not in the USA. Audre became the firm friend of Dagmar for several years afterwards.

But in the meantime, she underwent another episode of depression. At this point her daughter Beth was preparing for her first year at Harvard University. Audre and Frances disagreed about the children: while Audre still wanted to be able to offer both of them a home to come back to after university, Frances did not. But Frances was truly loyal to Audre, putting on a large party for the launch of *Zami*, which was held on the Hunter campus at Eleanor Roosevelt House, with 100 guests. It was a splendid occasion.

But her relationship with Frances was coming to an end. In March 1981 she had visited St Croix, for the Women Writers Symposium. There she had met Gloria Joseph, and stayed at her home. The invasion of Grenada in October 1983, by the USA led by Ronald Reagan, was appalling to Audre: it brought her closer to Gloria, who visited New York after the invasion to see relatives, and talked to Audre as well. They decided to visit Grenada together on a fact-finding mission, on 16th December, only two months later, which they found horrifying. Gloria also arranged a public 'conversation' between Audre and the African American writer and activist James Baldwin. James was a homosexual, though this did not come out in the published version of their dialogue, in *Essence*.

It was now six years since her breast cancer operation, and Audre had been very careful with her diet, but at the beginning of 1984 she was having digestive problems. Her oncologist discovered a liver tumour, which was reckoned to be metastatic from her original breast cancer. She was referred to Dr Kurtz, a liver tumour specialist, for a biopsy. But she found his manner unhelpful, and resisted the biopsy, going off to the library to do as much research as she could into liver tumours. Also, she was about to go to Germany where she met up again with Dagmar.

While in Berlin she wrote: 'I have been here a week, and already a whole new life has begun…'[25] She visited other European cities, including Zurich, answering questions about *The Cancer Journals*, and then returned to Berlin, where she began to have further liver problems. Dagmar suggested that she consult Dr Rosenblum, an anthroposophic doctor following in the footsteps of Rudolf Steiner. She agreed that Audre should not have a biopsy, instead recommending Iscador (extracts of mistletoe, commonly prescribed by orthodox oncologists in Germany), injected three times a week. Audre took on the injections, and they seemed to be working. On her return to the USA she had a second CAT scan, which showed that the tumour had not increased in size: this brought her hope that the Iscador injections were effective. She continued with her diet of fruit and vegetables.

Her book *Sister Outsider* gained excellent reviews, and she spent some time with Frances in Vermont in August. In February 1985 she went to St Croix again, staying with Gloria Joseph, and leaving behind some personal possessions. Audre was increasingly furious about the racist policies and behaviour in the USA, and also in South Africa, and spoke out about it in 'Apartheid USA', which was published by Women of Color Press in a series of pamphlets. Later that year she visited New Zealand and met up with Maori and Pacific Island women. She then went to Australia, where she voiced her solidarity with Aboriginal women, and spoke up for Aboriginal land rights.

In autumn 1985 Audre experienced renewed pain, and underwent another CAT scan, which revealed a second liver tumour. She consulted an anthroposophic doctor, Gerald Karnow, who confirmed that she had liver cancer. Karnow suggested a visit to the Lukas Klinik in Switzerland, which she attended, with financial support from her friends. In the meantime, on 13th December, there was a dedication of the Audre Lorde Women's Poetry Center at Hunter College. This was a wonderful occasion for Audre, with both Frances and Gloria present, as well as her children.

Then on 15th December she left for the Lukas Klinik with Frances, who checked into a local hotel. Audre spent nearly three weeks in the Klinik, undergoing a variety of therapies. But she now had to decide whether or not to stay with Frances, who smoked cigarettes and was not diet-conscious. Back in New York, Audre consulted a variety of doctors about her gall bladder and liver problems, with varying prognoses: one thought she might have five years' survival. In February 1986 she went with Gloria to Anguilla, in the British West Indies, for a fortnight's trip, in which she gloried in the heat, the sea and the sun. She then spent a further few days in St Croix with Gloria, before returning in April to take part in a conference on 'Caribbean Women: the Historical and Cultural Ties that Bind', organized by Gloria and three other women over a year, without institutional help. Audre wrote: 'It was a very inspiring experience for me, an ideal place for me to step out again, and I was so proud to be a part of it, and to speak and read my work as a Caribbean woman.'[27]

On 28th May her daughter Beth graduated from Harvard: a wonderful day for Audre. She wrote in *A Burst of Light*:

I'm proud of her, and I'm proud of having seen her thus far. It's a relief for me to know that whatever happens with my health now, and no matter how short my life may be, she is essentially on her way in the world, and next year Jonathan will be stepping out with his fine self, too. I look on them and they make my heart sing. Frances and I have done good work.[26]

In June 1986 Audre and Gloria went to the south of France with the Zamani Soweto Sisters from South Africa. She wrote in *A Burst of Light*, 'these women have taught me so much courage and perspective.'[28] Back in New York, a liver scan showed both tumours slightly smaller. On 6th November 1986 she wrote:

So I feel a sense of triumph as I pick up my pen and say yes I am going to write again from the world of cancer and with a different perspective—that of living with cancer in an intimate daily relationship. Yes, I am going to say… I have been diagnosed as having cancer of the liver, metastasized from breast cancer… The meaning of that diagnosis has become less important than how I live the life I have.[29]

She also wrote in *A Burst of Light*: 'Battling racism and battling heterosexism and battling apartheid share the same urgency inside me as battling cancer... I am learning to reduce stress in my practical everyday living. It's nonsense, however, to believe that any Black woman who is living an informed life in america can possibly abolish stress wholly from her life...'[30] In December 1986 she wrote: 'I believe that one of the ways in which cancer cells insure their own life and depress the immune system is by creating a physiologically engendered despair.'[31] But 'I visualize daily the battle going on in my body, and this is an important part of fighting for my life.'[32]

Audre was now spending more and more time with Gloria in St Croix, and eventually moved to St Croix permanently, leaving Frances on her own in Staten Island, after a 17-year partnership. The house was finally sold in 1988, and the relationship between the two came to an end. Audre spent the rest of her life in St Croix with Gloria, who carefully looked after her until she died, on 17th November 1992, 14 years after her original cancer diagnosis. A year before, she had been given the title of New York State Poet—the first woman and the first African American to be so honoured. Her body was cremated, and her ashes scattered in various places that she herself specified.

So to sum up: Audre's life was full of stress and depression, but she did her very best when she had cancer to investigate all the possibilities for treating it, orthodox and complementary, and in so doing extended her prognosis: her creative fire was not foiled. Her life also illustrates some important lessons for the 21st century about racism and feminism.

Select Bibliography

Rudolph P. Byrd, Johnnetta Betsch Cole, Beverly Guy-Sheftall (eds): *I Am Your Sister: Collected and unpublished writings of Audre Lorde* (Oxford University Press, New York, 2009)

Alexis de Veaux: *Warrior Poet: a biography of Audre Lorde* (W.W. Norton & Co., New York, 2006)

Audre Lorde: *Zami: A New Spelling of My Name: a Biomythography* (USA Persephone Press, 1982; Penguin Classics, 2018)

Audre Lorde: *The Audre Lorde Compendium: essays, speeches and journals (The Cancer Journals, Sister Outsider, A Burst of Light)* introduced by Alice Walker (Pandora, 1996)

Audre Lorde: *Your Silence Will Not Protect You* (Silver Press, 2017)

Audre Lorde: *The Black Unicorn* (poems) (W.W. Norton & Company Inc., New York and London, 1995)

Notes

1. *The Guardian*, 13th October 2008.
2. Lorde: *Zami: A New Spelling of My Name*, p. 17.
3. *ibid.*, p. 16.
4. *ibid.*, p. 59.
5. *ibid.*, p. 67.
6. Lorde: *Your Silence Will Not Protect You*, p. 136.
7. Lorde: *Zami*, p. 92.
8. *ibid.*, pp. 162–3.
9. *ibid.*, p. 122.
10. de Veaux: *Warrior poet*, p. 61.
11. Lorde: *Your Silence Will Not Protect You*, p. 1.
12. de Veaux: *Warrior Poet*, pp. 74–5.
13. *ibid.*, p. 166.
14. *ibid.*, p. 173.
15. *ibid.*, p. 192.
16. Lorde: *The Black Unicorn*, p. 31.
17. *ibid.*, p. 42.
18. Lorde: *Warrior Poet*, p. 259.
19. Lorde: *The Audre Lorde Compendium*, p. ix.
20. *ibid.*, p. 8.
21. *ibid.*, p. 10.
22. *ibid.*, p. 41.
23. *ibid.*, p. 58.
24. *ibid.*, p. 160.
25. *Warrior Poet*, p. 340.
26. *The Audre Lorde Compendium*, p. 285.
27. *ibid.*, p. 306.
28. *ibid.*, p. 310.
29. *ibid.*, p. 328.
30. *ibid.*, p. 333.
31. *ibid.*, p. 333.
32. *ibid.*, p. 334.

Conclusions

WHEN I FIRST HAD THE IDEA OF WRITING this book, about 20 years ago, there was plenty of anecdotal evidence that stress, trauma, anxiety and depression were risk factors for cancer, especially breast cancer, but there was little strictly controlled research on the subject. In 1990 the *British Journal of Hospital Medicine* published the proceedings of an international conference they held on 'Cancer and the Mind', where Maurice Slevin (MD, FRCP) wrote in his Preface:

> *It was clear, listening to the speakers, that there is no consensus view in this field. The meeting sparked considerable controversy with often diametrically opposed views being expressed, particularly on the relationship between personality and cancer development, and the alternative or complementary approaches to the treatment of cancer. What is clear is that much progress has been made and that serious research is now being conducted.*[1]

One piece of research published in the *British Medical Journal* five years later was by CC Chen et al., 'Adverse life events and breast cancer: case-control study', where it was found that 'all severe events and coping with the stress of adverse events... significantly predicted a diagnosis of breast cancer.'[2] Another study, published in 2004, however concluded that 'As yet, there is no sufficient evidence that any psychological factor irrefutably contributes to the development of cancer.'[3]

But the number of studies increased, and now there is clear evidence that there is a connection. One study puts the point thus: 'Chronic depression is associated with increased cancer risk and shortened survival.'[4] A second says: 'Depression affects one out of every six adults with women being affected twice as often as men.' Shortly afterwards, a table lists 25 studies on the subject of an association between depression and cancer.[5] Another study says: 'The results of 165 studies indicate that stress-related psychosocial factors are associated with higher cancer incidence in initially healthy populations.'[6] *But what do we do about it?*

One thing that has improved since my own diagnosis of breast cancer in 1986 is the much greater part played by cancer support groups in the healing process, and also, even in hospitals, the provision of complementary care for cancer patients. In Scotland, for instance, Maggie's Centres play an increasing part in the help available, offering all kinds of support, including counselling, group work, art therapy, stress management, and even walks in botanical gardens. Also, we now talk about cancer: there is no shame in having it. When I attended for radiotherapy in Guildford in 1987 I was not allowed to put a notice on the board about our local cancer support group, because 'some of the ladies don't know they have cancer'. I doubted this, but had to abide by the sister's instruction. But my main support came from what was then the Bristol Cancer Help Centre (now Penny

Brohn UK). Without the help they gave me, with dietary advice, supplements, and counselling, I doubt if I should still be here: I did not have a good prognosis. My personal cancer story has been told in *Fighting Spirit*.[7] But now, in 2019, I was able to nominate Penny Brohn for the Wall of Honour in the Royal Society of Medicine: I could not have done this 20 years ago.

However, there is still a huge lack of appropriate services available for people in the UK who have mental health issues, especially young people. I suggest that each GP practice should have a counsellor immediately available to discuss mental health with patients, instead of a six-month wait to see a mental health professional. In Scotland, one in four GP consultations are about mental health. Such issues, if they are dealt with straight away, may well not then be the seeds of future problems, including cancer. Also, there will be less need for the prescription of anti-depressants. Mental health is just as important as physical health: indeed, it often impinges upon it.

Another point that has surfaced during the writing of this book is the prevalence of feminist issues in the stories I have chosen. Women who have achieved something beyond the average have almost always had to face extra difficulties because of sexism. Even now, women are paid significantly less than men (despite equal pay legislation), and tend to do more housework and childcare, even when they earn more than their male partners. No wonder the rate of breast cancer has been going up during the last few years. As Mary Beard said in *Women and Power: a Manifesto*: 'women are still perceived as belonging outside power',[8] in spite of two female prime ministers in the UK in recent times.

Only a few women with breast cancer write books, or have books written about them. But the book I translated from French, published in 1994, by Patrice Guex, entitled *An Introduction to Psycho-oncology*, already spelt out the theme of this book, that 'Some research suggests that behaviour, life-style, social environment, and stress play a part in the onset of cancer.'[9] Guex also quoted LeShan, whose book I referred to in my introduction. Now that this is regarded as fact, not fantasy, we must take it seriously, both in our treatment of cancer patients, and even more important, in our treatment of mental ill health in young women. Their creative fire must not be foiled. As Professor Eysenck said in the conference *Cancer and the Mind* in 1990, 'we should be looking to preventive medicine rather than waiting until people are suffering from cancer before we try to do anything about it.'[10]

Notes

1. Preface to 'Cancer and the Mind': Proceedings of an international conference held by the British Journal of Hospital Medicine, ed. Maurice Slevin and Robert Short (Mark Allen Publishing Ltd, London 1990).

2. C.C. Chen, A.S. David, H. Nunnerley *et al.*: 'Adverse life events and breast cancer: case-control study', *British Medical Journal* vol. 311, 9 December 1995, 1527–30.

3. Bert Garssen: 'Psychological factors and cancer development: Evidence after 30 years of research', *Clinical Psychology Review* 24 (2004), 315–38.

4. M. Beatriz Currier and Charles B. Nemeroff: 'Depression as a Risk Factor for Cancer: from Pathophysiological Advances to Treatment Implications', *Annual Review of Medicine* 2014, 65, 203–10.

5. Brenda W.J.H. Penninx, Yuri Milaneschi, Fernice Lamers, Nicole Vogelzangs: 'Understanding the somatic consequences of depression: biological mechanisms and the role of depression symptom profile', *BMC Medicine* 2013, 11.129.

6. Y. Chida, M. Hamer, J. Wardle, A. Steptoe: 'Do stress-related psychosocial factors contribute to cancer incidence and survival?' *Nat. Clin. Pract. Oncol.* 2008, Aug. 5 (8), 466–75.

7. Heather Goodare (ed.): *Fighting Spirit: the Stories of Women in the Bristol Breast Cancer Survey*, with a Foreword by Sheila Hancock, OBE (Scarlet Press, London, 1996), pp. 113–29, 'The Search for Meaning'.

8. Mary Beard: *Women and Power: a Manifesto* (Profile Books Ltd, London, 2017), p. 56.

9. Patrice Guex, translated from French by Heather Goodare, with a Foreword by Karol Sikora: *An Introduction to Psycho-oncology* (Routledge, London, 1994), p. 6.

10. *Cancer and the Mind* (see ref. 1): H.J. Eysenck, 'Personality and Cancer Development', p. 9.

Heather Goodare: biographical note

Heather (born 1931) entered Christ's Hospital, Hertford, by Almoner's Nomination and competitive examination. She was a founder member of the National Youth Orchestra, going on to lead the second violins. She was appointed Head Girl in 1948, and read English at Lady Margaret Hall, Oxford (1949–52). She worked mainly as an academic editor, for Heinemann Educational Books (finally as Chief Editor), Longman, Ginn, BBC Publications, and the Open University (as Faculty Editor, Educational Studies).

In 1957 she married a Hungarian refugee music student, Otto Károlyi, who went on to become a distinguished musicologist. Around the time her son was born in 1971 she continued with freelance editorial and translation work at home. Her first marriage sadly broke up; eventually she met Kenneth Goodare, also through music, and remarried in 1978.

Diagnosed with breast cancer in 1986, she was treated locally in West Sussex and Surrey, and also visited the Bristol Cancer Help Centre for complementary care. She qualified as a counsellor in 1992 after postgraduate training at Brighton University. She has been a 'consumer' reviewer for the Cochrane Collaboration, in both breast cancer (her own experience) and stroke (that of her husband). She is a member of the British Holistic Medical Association and a Life Fellow of the Royal Society of Medicine.

From 1990 to 2003 she ran a cancer support group in Crawley, West Sussex, and for five years chaired Breast Cancer UK. She was the first patient representative on the *British Medical Journal* Editorial Board, from 1995 to 1999. She has written and peer-reviewed for medical and psychological books and journals, and written many articles on the patient's perspective in research, and Patient and Public Involvement (PPI); before moving to Edinburgh in 2003 she was a frequent speaker at medical conferences. Her publications include a translation from French of *An Introduction to Psycho-oncology* by Patrice Guex (Routledge 1994), and 'Improving Cancer Care', with Louise Nadim, original research published in the *Journal of Holistic Healthcare* in November 2006 — a joint enterprise between patients and healthcare professionals. In 2001 she contributed a chapter ('Patient heal thyself') to *Integrated Cancer Care: Holistic, complementary, and creative approaches*, ed. Jennifer Barraclough (Oxford University Press).

Her personal interest in medical research came about as a result of her visit to the Bristol Cancer Help Centre, where she participated in the flawed study of breast cancer patients published prematurely in September 1990 in *The Lancet* (Bagenal et al.). With others she formed the Bristol Survey Support Group (BSSG) to challenge the study's findings and the way it was publicized by the cancer charities.

A formal complaint from the BSSG to the Charity Commission was upheld, and new parameters put in place for sponsoring medical research by charities. *The Lancet* revised its statistical review procedures. The resulting publication, which she edited, was *Fighting Spirit: the stories of women in the Bristol breast cancer survey* (Scarlet Press 1996), with a foreword by Sheila Hancock OBE. She also took part in a television programme that challenged the study's results ('Cancer Positive' on Channel 4) and a similar radio programme on Woman's Hour.

Since moving to Edinburgh in 2003 to join family members her husband has suffered a stroke, and she served as a lay representative on the Trial Steering Committee of the third International Stroke Trial (based in Edinburgh). She has been a member of the Women's Environmental Network Scotland, and the Edinburgh Health Forum, a small voluntary group that she chaired, besides serving on the local community council.

Apart from her healthcare interests, she has been an enthusiastic gardener in a neighbouring 'back green', and for several years was Convener and Newsletter Editor of the Friends of the Meadows and Bruntsfield Links, which in 2015 achieved charitable status, as a Scottish Charitable Incorporated Organisation (SCIO). She recently retired from playing the violin in the Meadows Chamber Orchestra, which she joined on moving to Scotland. She has graduated from dinghy sailing to tall ships, with the Jubilee Sailing Trust, another charity, which specializes in offering opportunities to physically disabled people, and in which she has served as Watch Leader. The accompanying photograph by her brother (John Young, on a visit from Tasmania) shows her at the helm of a yacht without an engine on the Norfolk Broads.

Picture Credits

Cover image: Adobe stock. Cover design by Jonathan Sturm.

Anne of Austria, Queen of France. Portrait by Peter Paul Rubens, copy after a lost original painted c. 1620-1625. Public Domain.

Michel Sarrazin, physician and surgeon. This painting is usually thought to be of Michel Sarrazin, however there is some debate as to whether or not this is true. Public Domain.

Frances d'Arblay ('Fanny Burney') by her brother Edward Francisco Burney. Public Domain.

Christina Georgina Rossetti from a crayon drawing by Dante Gabriel Rosetti. Public Domain.

Photograph of Empress Viktoria: half-length portrait, standing by chair, with orders on dress by Thomas Heinrich Voigt in the Royal Collection. Public Domain.

Kate Greenaway, details unknown. Public Domain.

Vanessa Bell by George Charles Beresford. Public Domain.

Rachel Carson: Alamy stock image.

Kathleen Ferrier: Alamy stock image.

Joan Eardley photograph by Audrey Walker, The Scottish Gallery Collection, Edinburgh.

Susan Sontag: Alamy stock image.

Audre Lorde: Alamy stock image.

Heather Goodare photograph by her brother John Young.

Index

Lightning Source UK Ltd.
Milton Keynes UK
UKHW020243221120
373825UK00005B/416